Lesney's
MATCHBOX® TOYS

Regular Wheel Years, 1947-1969

with Price Guide

Charlie Mack

1469 Morstein Road, West Chester, Pennsylvania 19380

ACKNOWLEDGEMENTS

Special thanks to the following people who helped in the production of this book. These persons were responsible for loaning models from their collections, proofreading, general information and guidance on prices.

Douglas Congdon-Martin, Ed Force, Dayle Friedman, Jim Gallegos, Bob Hawkins, Pat Lamagna, Frank & Ruth Lenda, Everett Marshall III, Nancy & Peter Schiffer, Joe Soucy, Ray Sytch, Neil Waldmann, Wayne Wilson

Copyright © 1992 by Charlie Mack.
Library of Congress Catalog Number: 92-60637.

Printed in the United States of America.
ISBN: 0-88740-434-0

We are interested in hearing from authors with book ideas on related topics.

Published by Schiffer Publishing, Ltd.
1469 Morstein Road
West Chester, Pennsylvania 19380
Please write for a free catalog.
This book may be purchased from the publisher.
Please include $2.95 postage.
Try your bookstore first.

TABLE OF CONTENTS

INTRODUCTION

The toys pictured and listed in this book represent the major variations of the most popular series made by Lesney Products from 1947 to mid-1969.

The International scope of Matchbox® toys is quite apparent as one encounters catalogs, boxes, and labels for the toys printed in a dozen languages. Certain toys have been made for sale in specific stores, or to promote specific companies. Test markets are tried in selected countries and toys are sold in one part of the world before others. The numbering of the toys has been known to vary between catalogs for different countries. The result of all of these variables is a fascinating and infinite variety of Matchbox® toys.

The public's consistent enthusiasm, and the long-term interest of children grown to adults have provided the necessary ingredients for Matchbox® toys to become ideal collectible items. The old toys have become scarce and variations of newer toys have given the collectors a challenge to own each one. The collectors seek both toys and related catalogs, collector buttons, and boxes. Gradually, collectors were drawn by their common goals into organized clubs, a current list of which is included at the end of this book. The collector club magazines provide details of the countless variations as they are found and cataloged, and keep the members up-to-date on new toys released around the world.

A WORD ON VARIATIONS

In addition to the major variations listed in this text, there are countless casting, window, tire and base variations not listed. These changes occurred as tooling became worn or parts for a certain model were exhausted and available parts from other models were used to finish a production run of a certain model as opposed to destroying unfinished models.

Even different baseplates were substituted to finish a run of models. The 55B Police Car base can be found on the 59B Fire Chief Car and vise versa. Although uncommon, it is possible to find a model with more than one type or color of wheel. Also, there are many interchangeable parts such as plastic tires on 51B Hay Trailer and hooks on those fitted with plastic hooks. Drivers are also a common replaced part. There have been reproduction parts made including decals, tires, metal braces, drivers, and in some cases all parts to a complete model. It is important to realize that although most collectors and dealers are honest, learning to recognize a restored model is your best safeguard against paying too much for a model which appears to be genuine.

A WORD ON PRICING

Also please note the price guide included is the stated price for a mint and boxed model. A model mint and unboxed is usually worth slightly less (2-10% is a good rule of thumb). This does not dictate what should be charged for a model, but is only a guide. The local market usually determines the price which can be charged as prices can vary, say, in the U.S.A. vs. Europe. A model less than mint generally commands a price far less than the mint model depending on rarity. A chipped model generally has no collectible value but can be used as a "filler" until a mint model can be obtained. Joining a collectors club can be an excellent way to learn about current market values of models along with obtaining models at the most reasonable prices.

HISTORY 1947-1969

Leslie Smith and Rodney Smith were unrelated school friends when they were reunited by chance in 1940, both serving in The English Royal Navy. They each shared an ambition of one day having their own engineering factory, and discussed joining each other once the Second World War was over. Finally, they formed a partnership and began "Lesney Products" on June 19, 1947. The name was a composite of the founders' first names, and the word "Products" seemed appropriate because they had not yet decided what they would make. Leslie Smith was also employed by the J. Raymond Wilson Company which confirmed overseas orders, in a position he continued for several years. He worked in the evenings keeping the financial records of Lesney until Lesney Products grew sufficiently to support him full-time. Rodney Smith found employment with the engineering firm of Diecast and Machine Tools in London.

With about 600 pounds in combined revenue, the pair bought the old tavern "Rifleman" at Edmonton, London, and some government surplus die casting machinery. They now were determined to make pressure die casting products for industrial use.

Another employee at Diecast and Machine Tools was John W. Odell, always called Jack, who contributed his particular casting skill and joined into the Lesney venture. As subcontractors for industry, the three began producing small die-cast components. They were among many such small firms in London contributing to the rebuilding of the city.

The English business custom of taking stock inventory for taxation purposes on the first of January led to reduced orders for component suppliers during the last two months of the year. Therefore, the few Lesney employees were not kept busy producing die-castings during those months, and the founders considered alternate products. Some of the other small die-cast firms had made a few toys, and the Lesney people experimented with this, too. In 1948 the first of these toys was produced and sold locally in London in small shops. By 1952, Lesney was supplying a few toys to some of the Woolworth stores in London for the Christmas season.

The London toy distributors considered these little toys "Christmas cracker trash" and were not enthusiastic about handling them. Children, however, just loved them and the shopkeepers wanted more. By Christmas 1953, the Lesney people recognized that there was a market for their toys, but were not interested at this time in developing a sales force, storage facilities, and marketing techniques to distribute toys for a few months a year. They turned, instead, to agents who specialized in marketing to handle their toys. In the east end of London there were several agents well established long before the war. The one they contacted was Moko.

Moses Kohnstam was a German agent from Nuremberg who came to England in about 1900 to develop the toy industry. He specialized in packaging, storing, distributing, and financial backing for many small toy manufacturers; for this he received a percentage of the selling price. Moses Kohnstam's company was Moko, and the toys he distributed carried his company's name—*Moko,* no matter what various small firm made them.

When Lesney Products began manufacturing metal die-cast toys in 1948, it started with the Aveling Barford diesel road roller. By 1953, seventeen other toys joined the Lesney line. The variety of toys in this group reflects the uncertain direction of this branch of the company at that time. Mechanical animals, vehicles with wheels, and even a fishing novelty item were all tried before the success of the wheeled vehicles eclipsed efforts in the other directions.

Between 1950 and 1952, the English government restricted the use of zinc for non-essential products during the Korean War, and therefore no die-cast toys could be made. Only the tin "Jumbo-the-Elephant" was made by Lesney during this period.

During 1953, Jack Odell began designing smaller scale toys. The first were smaller versions of the original Lesney toys. These small toys were enormously successful, and were continued to become the 1-75 series. With the growing success of the small series, the larger toys were phased out by 1954.

Each of the early Lesney toys was packaged in a cardboard box which was printed with a picture of the toy, its name, and in some cases the name of the distributor of the toy—Moko. From a collector's point of view the toy is more interesting with its original box in good condition, and some have made a science of collecting the boxes.

In 1953, Moses Kohnstams' successor Richard Kohnstam was in charge of the Moko company. Lesney Products and Richard Kohnstam entered into an agreement whereby Moko would package and distribute the toys. Eventually, Moko became the sole distributor of the toys worldwide. This was the year that Lesney began the small 1-75 series of toys.

By 1954, Lesney produced eighteen models which were distributed by Moko. The trademark "Matchbox" had been registered in 1953 and belonged 50% to Moko who continued to provide its services and financial backing of the toys. Rodney Smith by now had moved to Australia and left Lesney, which was being managed by Leslie Smith and Jack Odell.

During 1958, Leslie Smith felt there was potential for the toys in Asia, particularly Japan, but Richard Kohnstam disagreed. In order to open up the market Lesney realized it had to go off on its own marketing course, so it must buy out the Moko interest in the toys. In 1959, Lesney concluded an agreement to buy "Moko", and produced their first catalog of toys. Since then Richard Kohnstam has formed his own firm—Riko. In 1959, a second catalog also was produced including the new Models of Yesteryear series. In 1954, distribution of Lesney toys to the United States was conducted by a salesman from New York named Fred Bronner. He became the sole U.S. importer during the late 1950's. In 1964, Lesney Products (U.S.A.) was formed as a division of the English Lesney Products. Lesney acquired all of Fred Bronner's stock and he became the first president of Lesney Products (U.S.A.).

It was in 1969 that the Fred Bronner Corporation became the Lesney Products Corporation in the United States. It was also in this year that Lesney Products faced their biggest competition, as it was in the late 1960's that Mattel introduced their Hot Wheels cars. As Matchbox cars didn't move fast at all down a track in 1969, it was do or die for the miniatures giant. This is an earmark event in Lesney history and it is at this point we break for this first in a series of three books.

BOOK #1—*Lesney's Matchbox® Toys:* "The Regular Wheel Years" (1947-1969)
BOOK #2—*Lesney's Matchbox® Toys:* "The Superfast Years" (1969-1982)
BOOK #3—*Universal's Matchbox® Toys:* "The First 10 Years" (1982-1992)

The original Lesney Products "Matchbox" toy factory at Eastway, in Hackney, London was first occupied by the Company in 1957. Nearly 1,000 people worked here by 1966 to produce over 50 million castings per year for the toys and for industrial companies throughout the world.

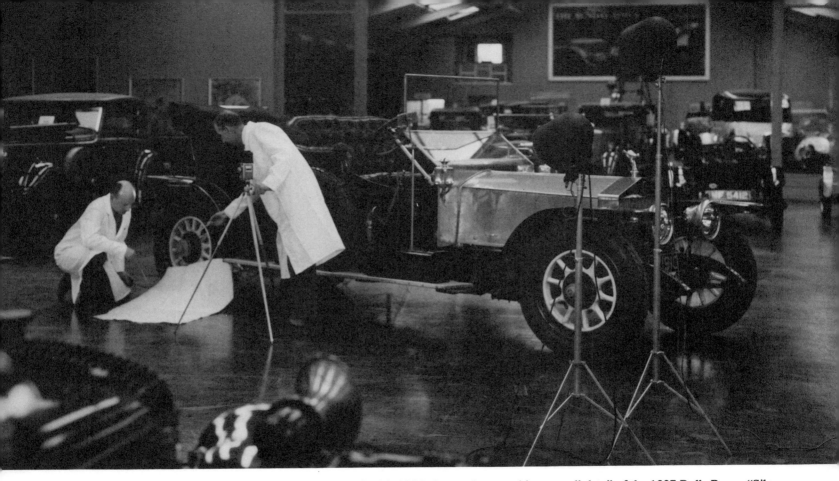

A chief "Matchbox" model designer Fred Rix is shown in this 1966 picture photographing a small detail of the 1907 Rolls-Royce "Silver Ghost" at the Measham Motor Museum near Burton-On-Trent, England. "Matchbox" modelmaker Ken Wetton is seen at the left checking a detailed measurement to ensure that the final "Matchbox" "Models of Yesteryear" replica of this car will be a completely true-scale miniature.

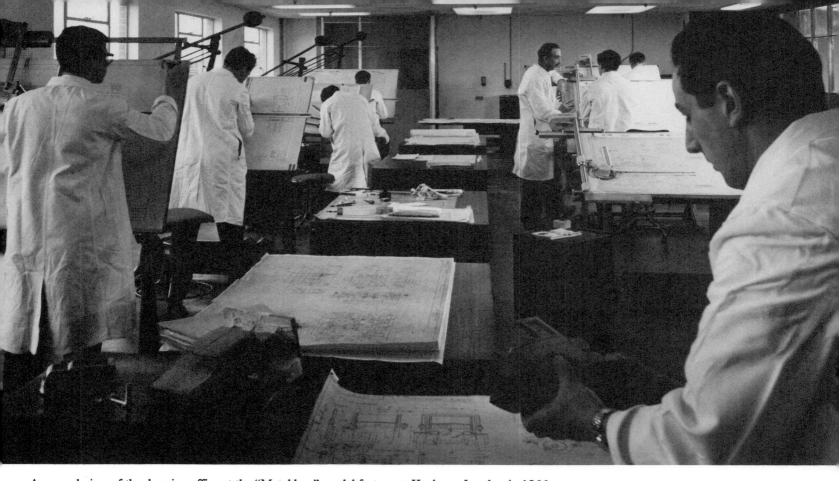

A general view of the drawing office at the "Matchbox" model factory at Hackney, London in 1966.

"Matchbox" prototype modelmaker Ken Wetton in 1966 carrying out a fine adjustment to a hand-made model of a proposed introduction for the "Models of Yesteryear" range.

Craftsmen pattern-makers hand carve detailed wooden patterns for new "Matchbox" Series models. Resin molds from these patterns are then used as guides for the cutting of the steel for the tools.

A craftsman pattern-maker checks a critical measurement on the wooden pattern for a new "Matchbox" Series model.

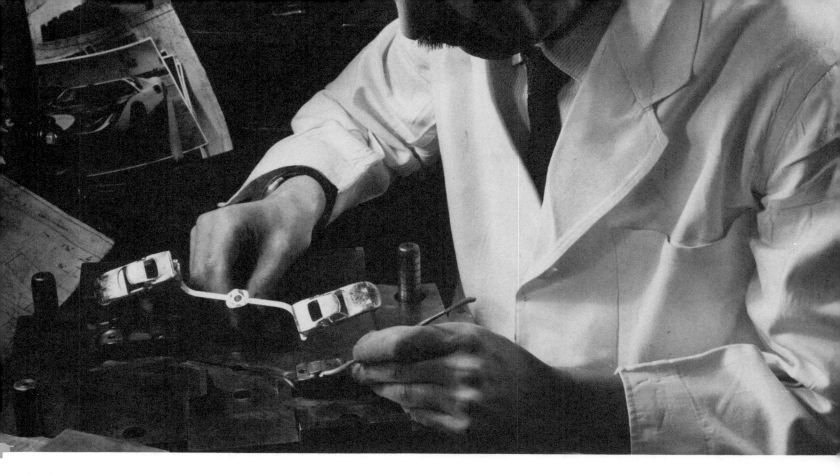

A skilled tool maker checks final details on one of the two-impression diecast molds.

The foundries in 1966 had 130 unique machines to produce the precision diecastings. The machines were designed and constructed by Lesney engineers. The output could exceed 10,000 "Matchbox" car bodies each day.

These unusual machines, designed and constructed by Lesney engineers, fit the tiny tires onto the wheel hubs.

Here, thousands of Jeep pick-up trucks are finished by an operator at a rivetting machine on the assembly line.

Automatic paint spraying machines gave each "Matchbox" miniature a complete coating of lead-free paint which was then oven-baked for maximum strength and quality finish.

This paint spraying machine in 1966 coated thousands of little "Matchbox" Caravan/Trailers. The multiple jets covered every corner and surface of the model and moved back and forth across the moving belt which passed into an oven where the lead-free paint was baked onto the toy.

Workers carried out the final assembly of the many detailed components in 1966 with the aid of many automated handling features.

Tiny decals and transfers were added by hand to bring the models to life. All the commercial vehicles have authentic color decorations which give them lifelike accuracy and detail.

Row 1 **Large Coronation Coach** (2)
Row 2 **Cement Mixers** (5, 3 & 6)
Row 3 **Ruston Bucyrus**
       Large Massey Harris Tractor

Row 1 **Soap Box Racer, Souvenir Letter Opener, Small Coronation Coach** (1)
Row 2 **Covered Wagon** (1), **Bread Bait Press** (3 & 1), **Covered Wagon** (2)
Row 3 **Road Roller** (2), **Caterpillar Bulldozer** (2), **Caterpillar Tractor** (3)
Row 4 **Prime Mover, Trailer & Bulldozer** (2)

Row 1 **Jumbo the Elephant**
Row 2 **Rag & Bone Cart** (1), **Large Milk Float** (1)
Row 3 **Muffin the Mule**

23

Row 1 1A-1 & 1A-2 **Diesel Road Rollers;** 1B-2 **Road Roller;** 1C-2 **Road Roller;** 1D-1 **Aveling Barford Road Roller;** 1E-1 & 1E-2 **Mercedes Truck**

Row 2 2A-1 & 2A-2 **Dumper;** 2B1 & 2B-2 **Dumper;** 2C-1 & 2-C2 **Muir Hill Dumper;** 2D-1 & 2D-2 **Mercedes Trailer**

Row 3 3A-1 & 3A-2 **Cement Mixer;** 3B-2, 3B-4 & 3-B3 **Bedford Tipper;** 3C-2 **Mercedes Benz "Binz" Ambulance;** 4B-1 & 4B-2 **Tractor.**

Row 4 4A-1 **Tractor;** 4C-1 **Sunbeam Motorcycle & Sidecar;** 4D-1 & 4D-2 **Dodge Stake Truck;** 5B-1, 5B-2 & 5B-3 **London Bus**

Row 1 5C-1, 5C-2, 5C-3, 5C-5 **London Bus**; 5D-4 & 5D-1 **London Bus**

Row 2 5D-3 **London Bus**; 6A-1 **Quarry Truck**; 6B-1 **Quarry Truck**; 6C-1 & 6C-2 **Euclid Quarry Truck**

Row 3 5D-2 & 6D-1 **Ford Pickup**; 7A-2 & 7A-3 **Horse Drawn Milk Float**; 7B-1, 7B-2 & 7-B3 **Ford Angila**

Row 4 7C-1 **Refuse Truck**; 8A-1, 8A-2 & 8A-3 **Caterpillar Bulldozer**, 8B-1 **Caterpillar Bulldozer**; 8C-1 & 8C-2 **Caterpillar Bulldozer**; 8D-1 **Caterpillar Bulldozer**

Row 1 8E-1 & 8E-2 **Ford Mustang Fastback**; 9A-1 **Dennis Fire Escape**; 9B-1 & 9B-2 **Dennis Fire Escape**; 9C-1 **Merryweather Fire Engine**

Row 2 9C-2 & 9C4 **Merryweather Fire Engine**; 9D-1 & 9D-2 **Boat & Trailer**; 10A-1 **Mechanical Horse & Trailer**; 10B-1 **Mechanical Horse & Trailer**

Row 3 10B-2 **Mechanical Horse & Trailer**; 10C-1, 10C-2, 10C-3 & 10C-4 **Sugar Container Truck** 10D-1 **Pipe Truck**

Row 4 10D-2 **Pipe Truck**; 11A-1, 11A-3, 11A-4, 11A-5 & 11A-6 **Road Tanker**, 11B-2 **Road Tanker**

Row 1 11B-3 & 11B-5 **Road Tanker**; 11C-1, 11C-2 **Jumbo Crane**; 11D-1 **Scaffold Truck**; 12A-1 **Land Rover**; 12B-1 **Land Rover**
Row 2 12B-2 **Land Rover**; 12C-1, 12C-2, 12C-3 & 12C-4 **Safari Land Rover**; 13A-1 **Wreck Truck**; 13B-2 **Wreck Truck**
Row 3 13C-1, 13C-2 & 13C-5 **Thames Wreck Truck**; 13D1, 13D-2 & 13D-4 **Dodge Wreck Truck**
Row 4 14A-1 **Daimler Ambulance**; 14B-1, 14B-3 & 14B-4 **Daimler Ambulance**; 14C-2 & 14C-3 **Bedford Ambulance**; 14D-1 **Iso Grifo**

Row 1 15A-1, 15A-2 & 15A-3 **Prime Mover**; 15B-2 **Atlantic Prime Mover**; 15C-3 **Refuse Truck**; 15D-1 **Volkswagen 1500 Saloon**; 16A-1 **Atlantic Trailer**

Row 2 16B-1 & 16B-3 **Atlantic Trailer**; 16C-1 & 16C-2 **Scammel Snow Plow**; 16D-1 & 16D-3 **Case Bulldozer**

Row 3 17A-3, 17A-1 & 17A-4 **Removal Van**; 17B-1 & 17B-2 **Removal Van**; 17C-1 & 17C-2 **Austin Taxi**; 17D-1 **Hoveringham Tipper**

Row 4 17E-1 **Horse Box**; 18A-1 **Caterpillar Bulldozer**; 18B-1 **Caterpillar Bulldozer**; 18C-1 **Caterpillar Bulldozer**; 18D-1 & 18D-2 **Caterpillar Bulldozer**

Row 1 18E-1, 18E-4 & 18E-3 **Field Car;** 19A-1 **MG Midget Sports Car;** 19B-1, 19B-2 & 19B-3 **MGA Sports Car**
Row 2 19C-3, 19C-4 & 19C-7 **Aston Martin Racing Car;** 19D-1 & 19D-3 **Lotus Racing Car;** 20A-5 & 20A-2 **Stake Truck**
Row 3 20A-1 & 20A-4 **Stake Truck;** 20B-1 & 20B-3 **686 ERF Truck;** 20C-5, 20C-4 & 20C-5 **Chevrolet Impala Taxi Cab**
Row 4 21A-1 **Long Distance Coach;** 21B-2 & 21B-3 **Long Distance Coach;** 21C-1, 21C-2, 21C-5 & 21C-7 **Commer Milk Float**

Row 1 21C-9 & 21C-8 **Commer Milk Float;** 21D-1 **Foden Concrete Truck;** 22B-1 **Vauxhall Cresta;** 22B-3 & 22B-2 1958 **Vauxhall Cresta**
Row 2 22B-5, 22B-7, 22B-8, 22B-6, 22B-9, 22B-10, 22B-12 1958 **Vauxhall Cresta**
Row 3 22B-13, 22B-14 & 22B-15 1958 **Vauxhall Cresta;** 22C-2 & 22C-1 **Pontiac Grand Prix Sports Coupe;** 23A-1 **Berkeley Cavalier Trailer;** 23B-1 **Berkeley Cavalier Trailer**
Row 4 23B-3 & 23B-4 **Berkeley Cavalier Trailer;** 23C-1, 23C-2 & 23C-3 **Bluebird Dauphine Trailer;** 23D-1 & 23D-2 **Trailer Caravan**

Row 1 24A-1 & 24A-2 **Weatherhill Hydraulic Excavator**; 24B-1 & 24B-2 **Weatherhill Hydraulic Excavator**; 24C-1 **Rolls Royce Silver Shadow**; 25A-1 & 25A-2 **Dunlop Van**
Row 2 25B-1 & 25B-3 **Volkswagen 1200 Saloon**; 25C-1, 25C-2 & 25C-3 **Petrol Tanker**; 25D-1 **Ford Cortina**
Row 3 25D-2 **Ford Cortina**; 26A-1 & 26A-2 **Concrete Truck**; 26B1, 26B-2 & 26B-4 **Foden Concrete Truck**; 26C-1 **G.M.C. Tipper Truck**
Row 4 27A-1 & 27A-2 **Bedford Lowloader**; 27B-1 & 27B-2 **Bedford Lowloader**, 27C-1 **Cadillac Sixty Special**

Row 1 27C-7, 27C-6 & 27C-8 **Cadillac Sixty Special;** 27D-1 **Mercedes 230SL;** 28A-1 & 28A-2 **Bedford Compressor Truck;** 28B-1 **Thames Compressor Truck**

Row 2 28B-2 **Thames Compressor Truck;** 28C-2 **Jaguar Mk. 10;** 28D-1 & 28D-2 **Mack Dump Truck;** 29A-1 & 29A-2 **Milk Delivery Van**

Row 3 29B-1, 29B-2 & 29B-3 **Austin Cambridge A55 Sedan;** 29C-1, 29C-2 & 29C-3 **Fire Pumper**

Row 4 30A-3, 30A-4 & 30A-2 **Ford Prefect;** 30B-2, 30B-3, 30B-5 & 30B-7 **Magruiz-Deutz Six Wheel Crane Truck**

Row 1 **30C-2 Magruiz-Deutz Six Wheel Crane**; 31A-1 & 31A-2 **Ford Station Wagon**; 31B-1, 31B-6 & 31B-5 **Ford Fairlane Station Wagon**

Row 2 31B-7 **Ford Fairlane Station Wagon**; 31C-1, 31C-2 & 31C-3 **Lincoln Continental**; 32A-1 & 32A-2 **Jaguar XK120**

Row 3 32A-3 **Jaguar XK120**; 32B-1, 32B-2 & 32B-4 **Jaguar XKE**; 32C-1 & 32C-2 **Leyland Tanker**

Row 4 32C-3 **Leyland Tanker**; 33A-3, 33A-2, 33A-5, 33A-6 & 33A-8 **Ford Zodiac Sedan**

Row 1 33A-10 **Ford Zodiac Sedan**; 33B-1, 33B-2, 33B-3 & 33B-4 **Ford Zephyr 6**; 33C-2 **Lamborghini Miura**
Row 2 33C-1 & 33C-3 **Lamborghini Miura**; 34A-1 & 34A-2 **Volkswagen Microvan**; 34B-1 & 34B-2 **Volkswagen Caravan**
Row 3 34C-1 **Volkswagen Camper**; 34D-1 **Volkswagen Camper**; 35A-1, 35A-2, 35A-3 & 35A-4 **Marshall Horse Box**; 35B-2 **Snow Trac**
Row 4 35B-3, 35B-1 & 35B-4 **Snow Trac**; 36A-1 & 36A-2 **Austin A50**; 36B-2 & 36B-3 **Opel Diplomat**

34

Row 1 36C-1 **Opel Diplomat**; 37A-1 & 37A-2 **Coca Cola Truck**; 37B-1 & 37B-2 **Coca Cola Truck**; 37C-2 **Cattle Truck**
Row 2 38A-1, 38A-2, 38A-3 & 38A-4 **Karrier Refuse Collector**; 38B-1 & 38B-2 **Vauxhall Victor Estate Car**
Row 3 38B-3 & 38B-4 **Vauxhall Victor Estate Car**; 38C-1, 38C-2 & 38C-3 **Honda Motorcycle and Trailer**; 39A-1 **Ford Zodiac Convertible**
Row 4 39A-2, 39A-3 & 39A-4 **Ford Zodiac Convertible**; 39B-1, 39B-4 & 39B-3 **Pontiac Convertible**

Row 1 **39B-9** Pontiac Convertible; **39C-1 & 39C-2** Ford Tractor; **40A-1 & 40A-3** Tipper Truck; **40B-1 & 40B-2** Royal Tiger Coach
Row 2 **40B-3** Royal Tiger Coach; **40C-1** Hay Trailer; **41A-1 & 41A-2** D-Type Jaguar; **41B-1, 41B-2 & 41B-3** D-Type Jaguar
Row 3 **41B-5** D-Type Jaguar; **41C-1, 41C-2, 41C-3 & 41C-4** Ford GT; **42A-1 & 42A-2** Evening News Delivery Van
Row 4 **42A-3** Evening News Delivery Van; **42B-1 & 42B-2** Studebaker Lark Wagonaire; **42C-1** Iron Fairy Crane; **43A-1 & 43A-2** Hillman Minx

Row 1 43A-4 **Hillman Minx**; 43B-1, 43B-2 & 43B-3 **Aveling Barford Tractor Shovel**; 43C-1 & 43C-2 **Pony Trailer**
Row 2 44A-1, 44A-2 & 44A-3 **Rolls Royce Silver Cloud**; 44B-1, 44B-4 & 44B-2 **Rolls Royce Phantom V**
Row 3 44B-2 **Rolls Royce Phantom V**; 44C-1 **Refrigerator Truck**; 45A-2, 45A-5, 45A-6 & 45A-7 **Vauxhall Victor**; 45B-1 **Ford Corsair w/ Boat**
Row 4 45B-2 **Ford Corsair w/ Boat**; 46A-1, 46A-2, 46A-4 **Morris Minor 1000**; 46B-1, 46B-2 & 46B-3 **Pickfords Van**

Row 1 46B-4, 46B-5, 46B-6, 46B-7 & 46B-8 **Pickfords Van**; 46C-1 **Mercedes Benz 300SE**

Row 2 46C-2 **Mercedes Benz 300SE**; 47A-1 & 47A-2 **One Ton Trojan Van**; 47B-1, 47B-2 & 47B-3 **Ice Cream Canteen**

Row 3 47B-4, 47B-5 & 47B-6 **Ice Cream Canteen**; 47C-1 & 47C-2 **DAF Tipper Container Truck**; 48A-1 **Meteor Sports Boat & Trailer**

Row 4 48A-2 & 48A-3 **Meteor Sports Boat & Trailer**; 48B-1, 48B-3 & 48B-7 **Sports Boat & Trailer**; 48C-1 **Dodge Dump Truck**

Row 1 49A-1, 49A-2, 49A-4 & 49A-5 **M3 Personnel Carrier**; 49B-1 & 49B-2 **Mercedes Unimog**
Row 2 50A-2, 50A-1, 50A-4, 50A-6, 50A-8 & 50A-9 **Commer Pickup**
Row 3 50B-1 & 50B-2 **John Deere Tractor**; 50C-3 & 50C-2 **Kennel Truck**; 51A-1 & 51A-3 **Albion Chieftan**
Row 4 51A-4 **Albion Chieftan**; 51B-1 & 51B-2 **John Deere Trailer**; 51C-1, 51C-2 & 51C-3 **Eight Wheel Tipper**

Row 1 51C-4 **Eight Wheel Tipper**; 52A-1, 52A-6, 52A-4 & 52A-5 **Maserati 4CLT Racing Car**; 52B-1 **BRM Racing Car**

Row 2 52B-3 **BRM Racing Car**; 53A-1, 53A-2, 53A-3 & 53A-4 **Aston Martin**; 53B-1 **Mercedes Benz 220SE**

Row 3 53B-2 & 53B-4 **Mercedes 220SE**; 53C-1 **Ford Zodiac MK V**; 54A-1 **Saracen Personnel Carrier**; 54B-2 **Cadillac Ambulance**; 55A-1 **D.U.K.W.**

Row 4 55A-2 & 55A-3 **D.U.K.W.**; 55B-1 & 55B-4 **Ford Fairlane Police Car**; 55C-2 **Ford Galaxie Police Car**; 55D-2 **Mercury Police Car**

Row 1 56A-1, 56A-2, 56A-3, 56A-4 & 56A-5 **London Trolley Bus;** 56B-1 **Fiat 1500**
Row 2 56B-2 & 56B-3 **Fiat 1500;** 57A-3, 57A-1 & 57A-2 **Wolseley 1500;** 57B-2 & 57B-5 **Chevrolet Impala**
Row 3 57C-1 & 57C-3 **Land Rover Fire Engine;** 58A-1 & 58A-2 **BEA Coach;** 58B-1 & 58B-4 **Drott Excavator**
Row 4 58C-1 **DAF Girder Truck;** 59A-4, 59A-1 & 59A-2 **Thames Van;** 59B-1, 59B-2 & 59B-3 **Ford Fairlane Fire Chief Car**

Row 1 59C-3 **Ford Galaxie Fire Chief Car;** 60A-1, 60A-3, 60A-4 & 60A-6 **J-2 Morris Pickup;** 60B-1 **Site Hut Truck;** 61A-1 **Ferret Scout Car**

Row 2 61B-2 & 61B-3 **Alvis Stalwart;** 62A-1 General Service Lorry; 62B-1, 62B-2 & 62B-4 **TV Service Van**

Row 3 62C-1 & 62C-2 **Mercury Cougar;** 63A-1 **Service Ambulance;** 63B-2 **Foamite Crash Tender;** 63C-2 & 63C-1 **Dodge Crane Truck**

Row 4 64A-2 & 64A-2 **Scammell Breakdown Truck;** 64B-1 **M.G. 1100;** 65A-2 & 65A-1 **Jaguar 3.4 Litre Sedan;** 65B-2 **Jaguar 3.4 Litre Sedan**

Row 1 65B-2, 65B-3 & 65B-5 **Jaguar 3.8 Litre Sedan;** 65C-1 **Claas Combine Harvester;** 66A-1 & 66A-2 **Citroen DS 19**

Row 2 66B-1 **Harley Davidson & Sidecar;** 66C-1 & 66C-3 **Greyhound Bus;** 67A-1 **Saladin Armoured Car;** 67B-1 & 67B-2 **Volkswagen 1600TL**

Row 3 67B-3 **Volkswagen 1600TL;** 68A-1 **Austin MKII Radio Truck;** 68B-1 & 68B-2 **Mercedes Coach;** 69A-2 & 69A-1 **Commer 30 CWT Van**

Row 4 69B-1 **Commer 30 CWT Van;** 69B-3, 69B-3 & 69B-8 **Hatra Tractor Shovel;** 70A-1, 70A-5 & 70A-6 **Thames Estate Car**

Row 1 70B-1 **Grit Spreader**; 71A-1 **Austin 200 Gallon Water Truck**; 71B-1 & 71B-2 **Jeep Gladiator**; 71C-1 & 71C-2 **Ford Heavy Wreck Truck**; 72A-1 **Fordson Tractor**

Row 2 72A-2 & 72A-5 **Fordson Tractor**; 72B-1 **Standard Jeep**; 73A-1 **RAF Pressure Refueller**; 73B-2 & 73B-1 **Ferrari F1 Racer**; 73C-1 **Mercury Commuter**

Row 3 74A-4, 74A-5 & 74A-3 **Refreshment Canteen**; 74B-2, 74B-3 & 74B-4 **Daimler Bus**

Row 4 75A-1 & 75A-2 **Ford Thunderbird**; 75B-1, 75B-2, 75B-4 & 75B-5 **Ferrari Berlinetta**

Row 1 Y-1A-6, Y-1A-7, Y-1A-2 & Y-1A-5 **1925 Allchin Traction Engine;** Y-1B-1 & Y-1B-3 **1911 Ford Model T**
Row 2 Y-1B-5 **Ford Model T;** Y-2A-2, Y-2A-4 & Y-2A-5 **1911 "B" Type Bus;** Y-2B-2 & Y-2B-4 **1911 Renault Two Seater**
Row 3 Y-3A-1 & Y-3A-4 **1907 London E Class Tramcar;** Y-3B-1, Y-3B-2 & Y-3B-5 **1910 Benz Limousine**
Row 4 Y-3B-4, Y-3B-5, Y-3B-9, Y-3B-22 & Y-3B-20 **1910 Benz Limousine**

Row 1 Y-4A-1 & Y-4A-2 **Sentinel Wagon**; Y-4B-7, Y-4B-1 & Y-4B-4 **Shand Mason Horse Drawn Fire Engine**
Row 2 Y-4C-3, Y-4C5 & Y-4C6 **1909 Opel Coupe**; Y-5A-1, Y-5A-5 & Y-5A-6 **1929 LeMans Bentley**
Row 3 Y-5B-1, Y-5B-2, Y-5B-3, Y-5B-4 & Y-5B-6 **1929 4-½ Litre Bentley**
Row 4 Y-5B-7 & Y-5B-9 **1929 4-½ Litre Bentley**; Y-5C-1 **1907 Peugeot**; Y-6A-1, Y-6A-2 & Y-6A-3 **1916 AEC "Y" Type Lorry**

Row 1 Y-6B-1, Y-6B-2, Y-6B-4, Y-6B-3, Y-6B6 & Y-6B-9 **1928 Type 35 Bugatti**
Row 2 Y-6B-7 **1928 Type 35 Bugatti;** Y-6C-1, Y-6C-2 & Y-6C-5 **1913 Cadillac;** Y-7A-1 **Leyland 4 Ton Van**
Row 3 Y-7A-2 & Y-7A-5 **Leyland 4 Ton Van;** Y-7B-1, Y-7B-2 & Y-7C-4 **1913 Mercer Raceabout**
Row 4 Y-7B-5 **Mercer Raceabout;** Y-7C-1, Y-7C-3 & Y-7C-5 **1912 Rolls Royce;** Y-8A-1 **1926 Morris Cowley**
"Bullnose"

Row 1 Y-8B-1, Y-8B-2 & Y-8B-3 **1914 Sunbeam Motorcycle & Sidecar;** Y-8C-2 **1914 Stutz;** Y-9A-14 **Fowler Showman's Engine**
Row 2 Y-9A-5 & Y-9A-2 **Fowler Showman's Engine;** Y-9B-1 & Y-9B-2 **1912 Simplex**
Row 3 Y-9B-5 **1912 Simplex;** Y-10A-1 & Y-10A-4 **1908 Mercedes Grand Prix;** Y-10B-1 **1928 Mercedes Benz 36/220**
Row 4 Y-10B-2 **1928 Mercedes Benz 36/220;** Y-10C-1 **1906 Rolls Royce Silver Ghost;** Y-11A-3 & Y-11A-6 **1920 Aveling Porter Steam Roller;** Y-11B-4 **1912 Packard Laundalet**

Row 1 Y-12A-1 **1899 Horse Drawn Bus;** Y-12B-2, Y-12B-1 & Y-12B-5 **1909 Thomas Flyabout**
Row 2 Y-12B-4 **1909 Thomas Flyabout;** Y-13A-1 & Y-13A-2 **1868 American Locomotive;** Y-13B-1 & Y-13B-3 **1911 Daimler**
Row 3 Y-13B-5 & Y-13B-4 **1911 Daimler;** Y-14A-1 **1903 Duke of Connaught;** Y-14B-2 & Y-14B-5 **1911 Maxwell Roadster**
Row 4 Y-15A-1, Y-15A-3, Y-15A-8, Y-15A-7 & Y-15A-5 **1907 Rolls Royce Silver Ghost**

Row 1 Y-15B1 **Packard Victoria**; Y-16A4, Y-16A5 & Y-16A6 **Spyker**
Row 3 Preproductions of Y-13B **Daimler**; Y-6C **Cadillac**; Y-5 **Bentley 4-½ Litre**
Row 4 Preproductions of Y-3B **Benz Limo**; Y-4C **Opel Coupe**; prototype of Y-10C **Rolls Royce Silver Ghost**

Row 1 M-1A-1 **Earth Scraper** M-1A-2 **BP Autotanker;** M-2A-2 **Bedford Ice Cream Truck,** M-2B-5 **Bedford Tractor & York Trailer**
Row 2 M-2B-2 **Bedford Tractor & York Trailer;** M-3A-1 **Thornycraft Antar & Centurion Tank;** M-4A-1 **Ruston Bucyrus**
Row 3 M-4B-2 **GMC Tractor & Freuhof Hopper Train;** M-5A-4 **Massey Ferguson Combine Harvester**
Row 4 M-6A-1 **Pickfords 200 Ton Transporter;** M-6B-1 **Racing Transporter**

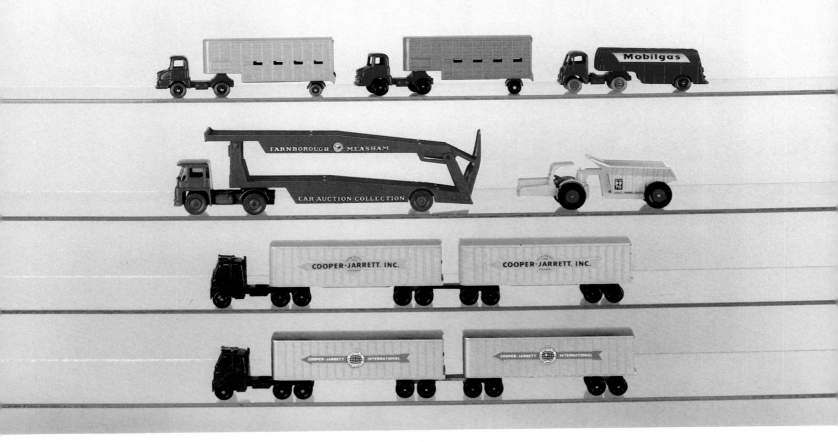

Row 1 M-7A-1 & M-7A-3 Cattle Truck; M-8A-1 **Mobilgas Tanker**
Row 2 M-8B-1 **Guy Warrior Car Transporter**, M-10A-2 **Dinkum Dumper**
Row 3 M-9A-2 **Interstate Double Freighter**
Row 4 M-9A-5 **Interstate Double Freighter**

Row 1 K-1A-1 **Weatherhill Hydraulic Excavator**; K-1B-1 **Hoveringham Tipper**; K-2A-2 **Muir Hill Dumper**; K-2B1 **KW Dump Truck**
Row 2 K-2C-2 & K-2C-3 **Scammell Heavy Wreck Truck**; K-3A-1 **Caterpillar Bulldozer**
Row 3 K-3B-1 **Hatra Tractor Shovel**; K-4A-1 & K-4A-3 **International Tractor**
Row 4 K-4B-2 **GMC Tractor & Freuhof Hopper Train**; K-4C-1 **Leyland Tipper**

Row 1 K-4C-2, K-4C-3 & K-4C-4 **Leyland Tipper; K-5A-2 Foden Dump Truck**
Row 2 K-5B-1 **Racing Transporter, K-6A-1 & K-6A-2 Allis-Chalmers Earth Scraper**
Row 3 K-6A-1 **Mercedes Benz "Binz" Ambulance; K-7A-1 Curtis Wright Rear Dumper; K-7B-1 Refuse Truck**
Row 4 K-8A-2 **Prime Mover and Caterpillar Tractor**

Row 1 K-8B-1 & K-8B-2 **Guy Warrior Car Transporter**
Row 2 K-8B-5 **Guy Warrior Car transporter;** K-9A-2 **Diesel Road Roller;** K-9B-2 **Claas Combine**
Row 3 K-9B-4 **Claas Combine Harvester;** K-10A-4 & K-10A-3 **Aveling Barford Tractor Shovel**
4 K-10B-1 **Pipe Truck;** K-11A-4 **Fordson Tractor & Farm Trailer**

Row 1 K-11B-1 & K-11B-2 **DAF Car Transporter**
Row 2 K-12A-1 & K-12A-2 **Heavy Breakdown Truck**; K-12B-1 **Crane Truck**
Row 3 K-13A-1 & K-13A-3 **Readymix Concrete Truck**; K-14A-2 & K-14A-1 **Jumbo Crane**
Row 4 K-15A-1 **Merryweather Fire Engine**; K-16A-1 **Dodge Tractor with Twin Tippers**

Row 1 K-17A-2 **Bedford Lowloader with Bulldozer**
Row 2 K-18A-1 **Articulated Horse Box;** K-19A-1 **Scammell Dump Truck**
Row 3 K-20A-1 **Tractor Transporter;** K-21A-1 & K-21A-2 **Mercury Cougar**
Row 4 K-22A-1 **Dodge Charger;** K-23A-1 **Mercury Police Commuter;** K-24A-2 **Lamborghini Miura**

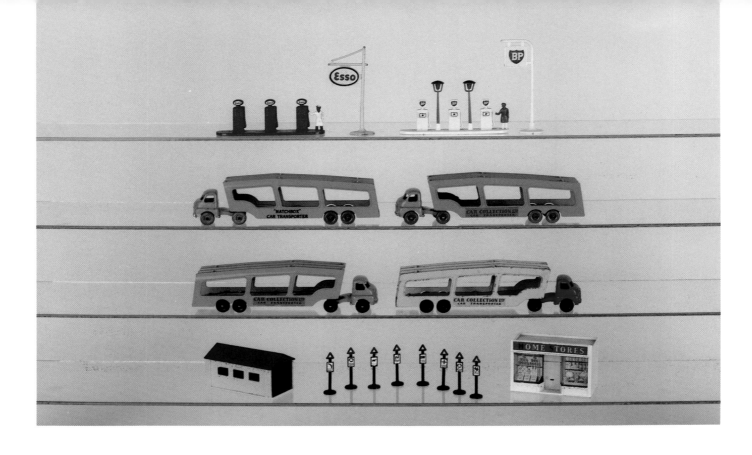

Row 1 A-1A-1 **Esso Pumps and Sign;** A-1B-1 **BP Pumps and Sign**
Row 2 A-2A-1 & A-2A-2 **Car Transporter**
Row 3 A-2A-3 & A-2A-4 **Car Transporter**
Row 4 A-3A-1 **Garage;** A-4A-1 **Road Signs;** A-5A-1 **Home Store**

Row 1 MG-1A-1 **Matchbox Garage**
Row 2 MG-1B-1 **Matchbox Garage**
Row 3 MG-1B-2 **Matchbox Garage**
Right:
Row 1 MF-1A-1 **Matchbox Fire Station**
Row 2 MF-1A-2 **Matchbox Fire Station**

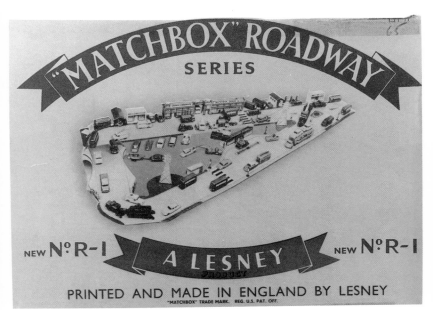

Left R-1B-1 **Roadway**
Right R-1A-1 **Roadway Layout**

Left R-1B-2 **Roadway**
Right R-1B-3 **Roadway**

Left R-2A-1 **Layout (Heart of London)**
Right R-2B-1 **Construction Site**

62

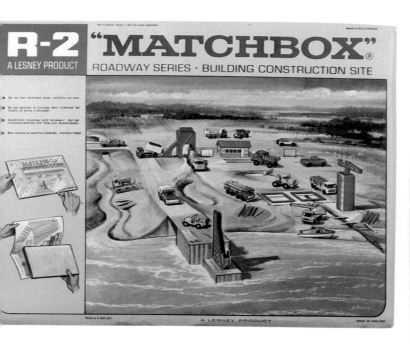

Left R-2B-2 **Construction Site**
Right R-3B-1 **Farm Site**

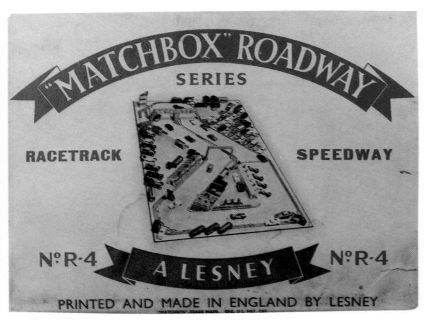

Left R-4A-1 **Racetrack Speedway**
Right R-4B-1 **Grand Prix Race Track**

G-6A Models of Yesteryear Gift Set & **G-7A1** Models of Yesteryear Gift Set

G-1A **Commercial Motor Set;**
G-5A1 **Army Set;** G-5A2 **Army Set**

G-2A **Car Transporter Set**
G-3A **Building Constructors Set;** G-4A **Farm Set**

G-1B Motorway Set

G-4B **Grand Prix Race Set**

G-7A2 Models of Yesteryear Gift Set
G-8A Construction Set

Row 1 **1957 pocket catalog, 1958 pocket catalog**
Row 2 **1959 (2nd edition) pocket catalog, 1960 pocket catalog**

Row 1 **1961 pocket catalog, 1962 pocket catalog, 1963 pocket catalog**
Row 2 **1964 pocket catalog, 1965 pocket catalog, 1966 pocket catalog**
Row 3 **1967 pocket catalog, 1968 pocket catalog, 1969 pocket catalog**

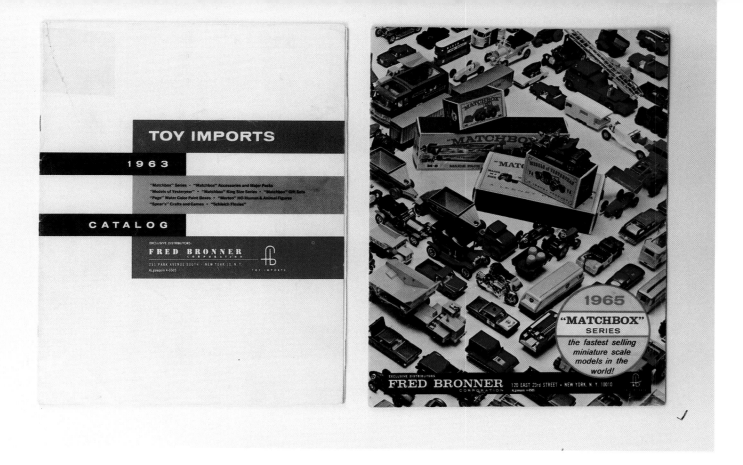

Left **1963 USA trade catalog**
Right **1965 USA trade catalog**

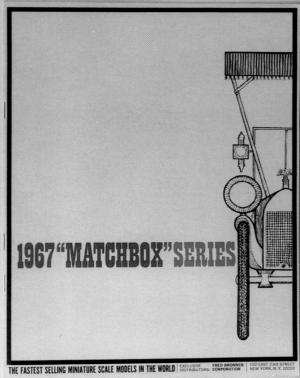

Left **1966 USA trade catalog**
Right **1967 USA trade catalog**

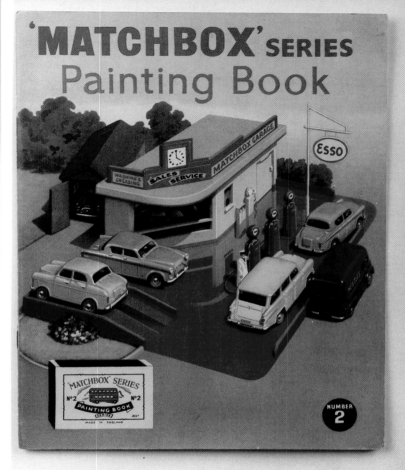

Left **1968 USA trade catalog**
Right **1969 USA trade catalog**

No. 2 Painting Book

Selection of different boxes including original design for Matchbox box in row 1

Row 1: **Blisterpacks from 1963 and 1966**
Row 2: **Blisterpacks from 1969**

Home Display five compartment case (1969)

PREPRODUCTION MODELS
Row 1 14C **Iso Grifo**, 14C **Iso Grifo**; 23B **Berkeley Cavalier Caravan**; 26C **GMC Tipper Truck**
Row 2 25D **Ford Cortina**; 47C **DAF Tipper Container Truck**; 52B **BRM Racing Car**; 53C **Ford Zodiac MK V**
Row 3 56B **Fiat 1500**; 58C **DAF Girder Truck**; 62C **Mercury Cougar**; 69B **Hatra Tractor Shovel**; 75B **Ferrari Berlinetta**
Row 4 K-1A **Weatherhill Hydraulic Excavator**; K-23A **Mercury Police Commuter**; K-4B **Leyland Tipper**

PROTOTYPES (ONE OF A KINDS)
Row 1 **Digger Crane**
Row 2 **Airport Tender; Dodge Cement Truck; Dodge Maintenance Truck; Refreshment Canteen**
Row 3 **Mercedes Container truck; mold & casting for 49B Unimog**
Row 4 **Wooden profile for K-24A Lamborghini Miura, Antique Combine Harvester**

Row 1: **Copies of A-4 Road Signs**
Row 2: **Fake examples of 12C Land Rover Safari, 51C 8-Wheel Tipper; 12A Land Rover and 2X 48B Sports Boat & Trailer**
Row 3: **Matchbox Boxing Figure; Matchbox Series plastic copy; Marx Match box construction set; Shadow Box copies of 9A & 11A**
Row 4: **Shadow Box copies of 10A, 15A, 16A, 4A & 2A**

Top views of a selection of the rarest regular wheels

Left **UK Matchbox and Matchbox U.S.A.**
Right **Matchbox International Collectors Association**
& American International Matchbox

Left **Pennsylvania Matchbox Collectors Club**
Right **Matchbox Collectors Club**

EARLY LESNEY TOYS

When Lesney Products was first founded in 1947, toys were only a sideline to a manufacturing business run by Leslie Smith, Rodney Smith and Jack Odell. It was Jack Odell who first came up with the idea to make toys in 1948. At this time, these toys were not called "Matchbox", as this name didn't transpire until 1953 when the first miniature models were released. Before "Matchbox" became used as a trademark and just after the trademark began in use, therefore 1948 through 1955, fifteen items were released and are classified as "Early Lesney Toys". Some of these models were later scaled down into the miniatures line while others were not. One, the Bread Bait Press, is not a toy but rather belongs in a fisherman's tackle box! A further item is a souvenir letter opener with a sliding inner sleeve that reveals a hidden tiny Matchbox box! As these are made by Lesney they best fit in this category.

EARLY LESNEY TOYS

Aveling Barford Road Roller   4 3/8"   1948
Cement Mixer   3-9/16"   1948
Caterpillar Tractor   3 1/8"   1948
Caterpillar Bulldozer   4 1/2"   1948
Horse Drawn Milk Float   5 3/8"   1949
Rag and Bone Cart   5 1/4"   1949

Soap Box Racer   3 1/8"   1949
Jumbo the Elephant   4"   1950
Prime Mover with Trailer & Bulldozer   18"   1950
Muffin The Mule   5 1/2"   1951
Large Coronation Coach   15 3/4"   1952
Small Coronation Coach   4 1/2"   1953
Massey Harris Tractor   7 13/16"   1954
Bread Bait Press   2"   1954
Covered Wagon   4 7/8"   1955
Souvenir Letter Opener   8 1/2"   196?

VARIATIONS

AVELING BARFORD ROAD ROLLER, issued 1948
  1. Green body, red painted wheels, yellow flywheel cast ($500-700)
  2. Green body, unpainted painted wheels, no driver cast ($300-450)
  3. Green body, unpainted painted wheels, with driver cast ($300-450)

CEMENT MIXER, issued 1948
  1. Pale green body, red barrel & handle, red wheels ($150-250)
  2. Dark green body, red barrel & handle, red wheels ($150-250)

3. Dark green body, red barrel & handle, yellow wheels ($150-250)
4. Dark green body, green barrel & handle, green wheels ($150-250)
5. Dark green body, green barrel & handle, red wheels ($150-250)
6. Red body, dark green barrel & handle, green wheels ($150-250)

CATERPILLAR TRACTOR, issued 1948
1. green body and rollers ($500-700)
2. dark yellow body and rollers ($200-300)
3. orange body and rollers ($200-300)

CATERPILLAR BULLDOZER issued 1948
1. pale green body, rollers and blade ($500-700)
2. orange body, rollers and blade ($200-300)
3. dark yellow body, red rollers and blade ($200-300)

HORSE DRAWN MILK FLOAT, issued 1949
1. orange body ($650-800)
2. blue body ($800-1200)

RAG & BONE CART, issued 1949
1. yellow body with red wheels ($850-1200)
2. green body with red wheels ($1500-1800)

SOAP BOX RACER, issued 1949
1. gold body, brown driver, metal wheels ($1800-2500)

JUMBO THE ELEPHANT, issued 1950
1. light gray body with windup key ($450-600)

PRIME MOVER WITH TRAILER & BULLDOZER, issued 1950
1. orange mover, orange trailer, all green bulldozer ($500-750)
2. orange mover, blue trailer, all orange bulldozer ($450-700)
3. orange mover, blue trailer, yellow dozer with red blade ($350-500)

MUFFIN THE MULE, issued 1951
1. cream body with painted features, puppet strings ($175-250)

LARGE CORONATION COACH, issued 1952
1. gold painted body, king & queen cast inside ($800-1200)
2. gold painted body, queen only cast inside ($250-450)
3. gold plated body, queen only cast inside ($400-600)
4. silver plated body, queen only cast inside ($500-750)

SMALL CORONATION COACH, issued 1953
1. silver plated body ($90-125)
2. pale gold plated body ($100-150)
3. gold painted body ($150-200)

MASSEY HARRIS TRACTOR, issued 1954
1. red body, beige wheels with black rubber tires ($500-750)

BREAD BAIT PRESS, issued 1954
1. red body, green wingnut & inner fixture, "Lesney Milbro" cast ($60-85)
2. red body, unpainted wingnut, green inner fixture, "Lesney" cast ($50-75)
3. red body, unpainted wingnut and inner fixture, "Lesney" cast ($50-75)

COVERED WAGON, issued 1955
1. dark green body with white cover, brown horses, no barrels ($90-125)
2. dark green body with white cover, brown horses, red barrels ($90-125)

SOUVENIR LETTER OPENER, issued (unknown- 1960's)
1. black handle, silver blade, Lesney U.K. address on silver band ($100-125)
2. black handle, silver blade, Fred Bronner address on silver band ($100-125)

REGULAR WHEELS THE MATCHBOX™ SERIES 1-75

The extraordinary success of the small coronation coach in 1953 encouraged Lesney personnel to proceed with plans to make small sized toys for the 1953 selling year. They began by making scaled-down versions of seven of their earlier toys in this order: (1-A) Diesel Road Roller, (2-A) Dumper, (3-A) Cement Mixer, (4-A) Massey Harris Tractor, (6-A) Quarry Truck, (7-A) Horse-drawn Milk Float, and (8-A) Caterpillar Tractor. The (5-A) London Bus was designed especially for this small series. These toys were immediately successful with the children, and more new toys were made each successive year.

When the personnel gathered to design a box for the new small toys, they struck on the idea of using a style resembling a match box. This was not a new thought, for earlier in the 1900s toys from Germany were made with this style box. The Lesney people did, however, register the name "Matchbox" for this series and that name has identified their toys since. Lesney Products was then using the distribution and packaging facilities of Moko for its toys, and Moko had a significant financial interest in the new series.

The actual design of the printing on the box is not known to have derived from a Scandinavian match box cover for Norvic Safety Matches.

From this design, the Lesney and Moko people substituted their own wording and created the first Matchbox box. The front and back are yellow with red letters "Matchbox Series" in an arch above a black and red drawing of each toy inside. On both sides of the drawing, the number of the toy in this series is placed. Below the drawing, a scroll with lettering "A Moko Lesney" appears. The word "Product" is in a small arch below the scroll. For this design, the word Moko is written in script lettering. This box design was used only for the first seven toys in the Matchbox series which were made in 1953 and 1954.

1A Diesel Road Roller   1 7/8"   1953
1B Road Roller   2 1/4"   1955
1C Road Roller   2 3/8"   1958
1D Aveling Barford Road Roller   2 5/8"   1962
1E Mercedes Benz Lorry   3"   1968

2A Dumper   1 5/8"   1953
2B Dumper   1 7/8"   1957
2C Muir Hill Dumper   2 1/6"   1961
2D Mercedes Trailer   3 1/2"   1968

3A Cement Mixer   1 5/8"   1953
3B Bedford Tipper   2 1/2"   1961
3C Mercedes Benz "Binz" Ambulance   2 7/8"   1968

4A Massey Harris Tractor   1 5/8"   1954
4B Massey Harris Tractor   1 5/8"   1957
4C Triumph Motorcycle & Sidecar   2 1/8"   1960
4D Dodge Stake Truck   2 7/8"   1967

5A London Bus   2"   1954
5B London Bus   2 1/4"   1957
5C London Bus   2-9/16"   1961
5D London Bus   2 3/4"   1965

6A Quarry Truck   2 1/8"   1954
6B Quarry Truck   2 1/2"   1957
6C Euclid Quarry Truck   2 5/8"   1964
6D Ford Pickup   2 3/4"   1968

7A Horse Drawn Milk Float   2 1/4"   1954
7B Ford Anglia   2 5/8"   1961
7C Ford Refuse Truck   3"   1966

8A Caterpillar Tractor   1 1/2"   1955
8B Caterpillar Tractor   1 5/8"   1959
8C Caterpillar Tractor   1 7/8"   1961
8D Caterpillar Tractor   2"   1964
8E Ford Mustang Fastback   2 7/8"   1966

9A Dennis Fire Escape   2 1/4"   1955
9B Dennis Fire Escape   2 3/8"   1957
9C Merryweather Marquis Fire Engine   2 1/2"   1959
9D Boat and Trailer   3 1/4"   1966

10A Mechanical Horse and Trailer   2 3/8"   1955
10B Mechanical Horse and Trailer   2 15/16"   1958
10C Sugar Container Truck   2 5/8"   1961
10D Pipe Truck   2 7/8"   1966

11A Road Tanker   2"   1955
11B Road Tanker   2 1/2"   1958

11C Jumbo Crane   3"   1965
11D Scaffold Truck   2 1/2"   1969

12A Land Rover   1 3/4"   1955
12B Land Rover   2 1/4"   1959
12C Safari Land Rover   2 1/3"   1965

13A Bedford Wreck Truck   2"   1955
13B Bedford Wreck Truck   2 1/8"   1958
13C Thames Wreck Truck   2 1/2"   1961
13D Dodge Wreck Truck   3"   1965

14A Daimler Ambulance   1 7/8"   1956
14B Daimler Ambulance   2 5/8"   1958
14C Bedford Ambulance   2 5/8"   1962
14D Iso Grifo   3"   1968

15A Prime Mover   2 1/8"   1956
15B Atlantic Prime Mover   2 5/8"   1959
15C Refuse Truck   2 1/2"   1963
15D Volkswagen 1500 Saloon   2 7/8"   1968

16A Atlantic Trailer   3 1/8"   1956
16B Atlantic Trailer   3 1/4"   1957
16C Scammell Mountaineer Snowplow   3"   1964
16D Case Bulldozer   2 1/2"   1969

17A Bedford Removals Van   2 1/8"   1956
17B Bedford Removals Van   2 1/8"   1958
17C Austin Taxi Cab   2 1/4"   1960
17D Hoveringham Tipper   2 7/8"   1963
17E Horse Box   2 3/4"   1969

18A Caterpillar Bulldozer   1 7/8"   1956
18B Caterpillar Bulldozer   2"   1958
18C Caterpillar Bulldozer   2 1/4"   1961
18D Caterpillar Bulldozer   2 3/8"   1964

18E Field Car   2 5/8"   1969

19A MG Sports Car   2"   1956
19B MGA SPorts Car   2 1/4"   1958
19C Aston Martin Racing Car   2 1/2"   1961
19D Lotus Racing Car   2 3/4"   1966

20A Stake Truck   2 3/8"   1956
20B ERF 686 Truck   2 5/8"   1959
20C Chevrolet Impala Taxi Cab   3"   1965

21A Long Distance Coach   2 1/4"   1956
21B Long Distance Coach   2 5/8"   1958
21C Commer Milk Truck   2 1/4"   1961
21D Foden Concrete Truck   3"   1968

22A Vauxhall Cresta   2 1/2"   1956
22B 1958 Vauxhall Cresta   2 5/8"   1958
22C Pontiac Grand Prix Sports Coupe   3"   1964

23A Berkeley Cavalier Trailer   2 1/2"   1956
23B Berkeley Cavalier Trailer   2 1/2"   1958
23C Bluebird Dauphine Trailer   2 1/2"   1960
23D Trailer Caravan   2 7/8"   1965

24A Weatherhill Hydraulic Excavator   2 3/8"   1956
24B Weatherhill Hydraulic Excavator   2 5/8"   1959
24C Rolls Royce Silver Shadow   3"   1967

25A Dunlop Van   2 1/8"   1956
25B Volkswagen 1200 Sedan   2 1/2"   1960
25C Petrol Tanker   3"   1964
25D Ford Cortina   2 7/8"   1968

26A Concrete Truck   1 3/4"   1956
26B Foden Concrete Truck   2 1/2"   1961
26C G.M.C. Tipper truck   2 5/8"   1968

27A Bedford Lowloader   3 1/8"   1956
27B Bedford Lowloader   3 3/4"   1959
27C Cadillac Sixty Special   2 3/4"   1960
27D Mercedes Benz 230SL   3"   1966

28A Bedford Compressor Truck   1 3/4"   1956
28B Thames Compressor Truck   2 3/4"   1959
28C Mark 10 Jaguar   2 3/4"   1964
28D Mack Dump Truck   2 5/8"   1968

29A Bedford Milk Delivery Van   2 1/4"   1956
29B Austin A55 Cambridge Sedan   2 3/4"   1961
29C Fire Pumper   3"   1966

30A Ford Prefect   2 1/4"   1956
30B Magiruz Deutz 6-Wheel Crane Truck   2 5/8"   1961
30C 8-Wheel Crane Truck   3"   1965

31A Ford Station Wagon   2 5/8"   1957
31B Ford Fairlane Station Wagon   2 3/4"   1960
31C Lincoln Continental   2 7/8"   1964

32A Jaguar XK140 Coupe   2 3/8"   1957
32B Jaguar XKE   2 5/8"   1962
32C Leyland Petrol Tanker   3"   1968

33A Ford Zodiac MKII Sedan   2 5/8"   1957
33B Ford Zephyr 6 MKIII   2 5/8"   1963
33C Lamborghini Miura   2 3/4"   1969

34A Volkswagen Microvan   2 1/4"   1957
34B Volkswagen Camper   2 3/5"   1962
34C Volkswagen Camper   2 5/8"   1967
34D Volkswagen Camper   2 5/8"   1968

35A Marshall Horse Box   2"   1957
35B Snow Trac Tractor   2 3/8"   1964

36A Austin A50   2 3/8"   1957
36B Lambretta Scooter & Sidecar   2"   1961
36C Opel Diplomat   2 3/4"   1966

37A Coca Cola Lorry   2 1/4"   1956
37B Coca Cola Lorry   2 1/4"   1960
37C Dodge Cattle Truck   2 1/2"   1966

38A Karrier Refuse Collector   2 3/8"   1957
38B Vauxhall Victor Estate Car   2 5/8"   1963
38C Honda Motorcycle & Trailer   2 7/8"   1967

39A Ford Zodiac Convertible   2 5/8"   1957
39B Pontiac Convertible   2 3/4"   1962
39C Ford Tractor   2 1/8"   1967

40A Bedford Tipper truck   2 1/8"   1957
40B Leyland Royal Tiger Coach   3"   1961
40C Hay Trailer   3 1/4"   1967

41A D Type Jaguar   2 3/16"   1957
41B D Type Jaguar   2 7/16"   1960
41C Ford GT   2 5/8"   1965

42A Bedford Evening News Van   2 1/4"   1957
42B Studebaker Lark wagonaire   3"   1965
42C Iron Fairy Crane   3"   1969

43A Hillman Minx   2 5/8"   1958
43B Aveling Barford Tractor Shovel   2 5/8"   1962
43C Pony Trailer   2 5/8"   1968

44A Rolls Royce Silver Cloud   2 5/8"   1958
44B Rolls Royce Phantom V   2 7/8"   1964

44C G.M.C. Refrigerator Truck   2 13/16"   1967

45A Vauxhall Victor   2 3/8"   1958
45B Ford Corsair w/ Boat   2 3/8"   1965

46A Morris Minor 1000   2"   1958
46B Pickfords Removal Van   2 5/8"   1960
46C Mercedes Benz 300 SE   2 7/8"   1968

47A 1 Ton Trojan Van   2 1/4"   1958
47B Commer Ice Cream Canteen   2 1/2"   1963
47C DAF Tipper Container Truck   3"   1968

48A Meteor Sports Boat & Trailer   2 3/8"   1958
48B Sports Boat & Trailer   2 5/8"   1961
48C Dodge Dumper Truck   3"   1966

49A M3 Personnel Carrier   2 1/2"   1958
49B Mercedes Unimog   2 3/8"   1967

50A Commer Pickup   2 1/2"   1958
50B John Deere Tractor   2 1/8"   1964
50C Ford Kennel Truck   2 3/4"   1969

51A Albion Chieftan   2 1/2"   1958
51B John Deere Trailer   2 5/8"   1964
51C 8-Wheel Tipper   3"   1969

52A Maserati 4CLT Racer   2 3/8"   1958
52B BRM Racing Car   2 5/8"   1965

53A Aston Martin   2 1/2"   1958
53B Mercedes Benz 220 SE   2 3/4"   1963
53C Ford Zodiac MK IV   2 3/4"   1968

54A Saracen Personnel Carrier   2 1/4"   1958
54B S & S Cadillac Ambulance   2 7/8"   1965

55A D.U.K.W. 2 3/4" 1958
55B Ford Fairlane Police Car 2 5/8" 1963
55C Ford Galaxie Police Car 2 7/8" 1966
55D Mercury Police Car 3" 1968

56A London Trolley Bus 2 5/8" 1958
56B Fiat 1500 2 1/2" 1965

57A Wolseley 1500 2 1/8" 1958
57B Chevrolet Impala 2 3/4" 1961
57C Land Rover Fire Truck 2 1/2" 1966

58A BEA Coach 2 1/2" 1958
58B Drott Excavator 2 5/8" 1962
58C DAF Girder Truck 3" 1968

59A Ford Thames Van 2 1/8" 1958
59B Ford Fairlane Fire Chief Car 2 5/8" 1963
59C Ford Galaxie Fire Chief Car 2 7/8" 1966

60A Morris J2 Pickup 2 1/4" 1958
60B Site Hut Truck 2 1/2" 1966

61A Ferret Scout Car 2 1/4" 1959
61B Alvis Stalwart 2 5/8" 1966

62A General Service Lorry 2 5/8" 1959
62B TV Service Van 2 1/2" 1963
62C Mercury Cougar 3" 1968

63A Ford Service Ambulance 2 1/2" 1959
63B Foamite Crash Tender 2 1/4" 1964
63C Dodge Crane Truck 3" 1968

64A Scammell Breakdown Truck 2 1/2" 1959
64B MG 1100 2 5/8" 1966

65A Jaguar 3.4 Litre Saloon 2 1/2" 1959
65B Jaguar 3.4 Litre Saloon 2 5/8" 1962
65C Claas Combine Harvester 3" 1967

66A Citroen DS19 2 1/2" 1959
66B Harley Davidson Motorcycle & Sidecar 2 5/8" 1962
66C Greyhound Bus 3" 1967

67A Saladin Armoured Car 2 1/2" 1959
67B Volkswagen 1600 TL 2 3/4" 1967

68A Austin MKII Radio Truck 2 3/8" 1959
68B Mercedes Coach 2 7/8" 1965

69A Commer 30 CWT Van 2 1/4" 1959
69B Hatra Tractor Shovel 3" 1965

70A Ford Thames Estate Car 2 1/8" 1959
70B Ford Grit Spreader 2 5/8" 1966

71A Austin 200 Gallon Water Truck 2 3/8" 1959
71B Jeep Gladiator Pickup 2 5/8" 1964
71C Ford Heavy Wreck Truck 3" 1968

72A Fordson Tractor 2" 1959
72B Standard Jeep 2 3/8" 1966

73A 10 Ton Pressure Refueller 2 5/8" 1959
73B Ferrari F1 Racing Car 2 5/8" 1962
73C Mercury Station Wagon 3" 1968

74A Mobile Refreshment Canteen 2 5/8" 1959
74B Daimler Bus 3" 1966

75A Ford Thunderbird 2 5/8" 1960
75B Ferrari Berlinetta 2 3/4" 1965

VARIATIONS

1A DIESEL ROAD ROLLER, issued 1953
1. dark green body, red metal wheels ($35-50)
2. light green body, red metal wheels ($75-100)

1B ROAD ROLLER, issued 1955
1. light green body, red metal wheels, dark tan driver ($50-75)
2. light green body, red metal wheels, light tan driver ($50-75)

1C ROAD ROLLER, issued 1958
1. light green body, red metal wheels ($40-60)
2. dark green body, red metal wheels ($40-60)

1D AVELING BARFORD ROAD ROLLER, issued 1962
1. dark green body, red plastic rollers ($12-18)

1E MERCEDES BENZ LORRY, issued 1968
1. mint green body, orange canopy ($5-8)
2. mint green body, yellow canopy ($8-12)

2A DUMPER, issued 1953
1. green body, red dump, green metal wheels ($125-150)
2. green body, red dump, unpainted metal wheels ($35-50)

2B DUMPER, issued 1957
1. green body, red dump, unpainted metal wheels, no.2 cast ($35-40)
2. green body, red dump, gray plastic wheels, no.2 cast ($35-40)

2C MUIR HILL DUMPER, issued 1961
1. red cab, green dump, black plastic wheels, "Laing" decals ($15-18)
2. red cab, green dump, black plastic wheels, "Muir Hill" decals ($50-75)

2D MERCEDES TRAILER, issued 1968
1. mint green body, orange canopy ($5-8)
2. mint green body, yellow canopy ($8-12)

3A CEMENT MIXER, issued 1953
1. Blue body & barrel, orange metal wheels ($25-35)
2. Blue body & barrel, gray plastic wheels ($35-45)

3B BEDFORD TIPPER, issued 1961
1. gray cab, maroon dump, gray plastic wheels ($90-110)
2. gray cab, red dump, gray plastic wheels ($18-25)
3. gray cab, maroon dump, black plastic wheels ($12-15)
4. gray cab, red dump, black plastic wheels ($12-15)

3C MERCEDES BENZ "BINZ" AMBULANCE issued 1968
1. off white body, red cross decals ($5-8)
2. off white body, red cross decals ($5-8)
3. cream body, red cross decals ($5-8)
4. cream body, red cross labels ($5-8)

4A MASSEY HARRIS TRACTOR, issued 1954
1. red body, rear fenders cast, metal wheels ($35-50)

4B MASSEY HARRIS TRACTOR, issued 1957
1. red body, no fenders cast, no.4 cast, metal wheels ($35-50)
2. red body, no fenders cast, no.4 cast, gray plastic wheels ($45-60)

4C TRIUMPH MOTORCYCLE & SIDECAR, issued 1960
1. silver blue body, black plastic tires ($35-50)
2. dark silver blue body, black plastic tires ($35-50)

4D DODGE STAKE TRUCK, issued 1967
1. yellow cab, blue-green stakes ($50-75)
2. yellow cab, green stakes ($5-8)

5A LONDON BUS, issued 1954
1. red body, "Buy Matchbox series" labels ($50-65)

5B LONDON BUS, issued 1957
1. red body, "Buy Matchbox Series" decals, metal wheels ($45-60)
2. red body, "Buy Matchbox Series" decals, gray plastic wheels ($60-75)

3. red body, "Players Please" decals, gray plastic wheels ($85-100)
4. red body, "Visco static" decals, gray plastic wheels ($125-150)

5C LONDON BUS, issued 1961
1. red body, "Player's Please" decals, gray plastic wheels ($100-125)
2. red body, "Visco Static" decals, gray plastic wheels ($35-45)
3. red body, "Drink Peardrax" decals, gray plastic wheels ($125-175)
4. red body, "Drink Peardrax" decals, black plastic wheels ($125-175)
5. red body, "Baron of Beef" decals, gray plastic wheels ($175-200)
6. red body, "Baron of Beef" decals, black plastic wheels ($175-200)
7. red body, "Visco Static" decals, black plastic wheels ($25-40)

5D LONDON BUS, issued 1965
1. red body, "Longlife" decals, black plastic wheels ($8-12)
2. red body, "Visco Static" decals, black plastic wheels ($8-12)
3. red body, "Visco static" labels, black plastic wheels ($8-12)
4. red body, "Baron of Beef" decals, black plastic wheels ($175-200)

6A QUARRY TRUCK, issued 1954
1. orange cab, gray dump, metal wheels ($25-40)
2. orange cab, gray dump, gray plastic wheels ($150-200)

6B QUARRY TRUCK, issued 1957
1. yellow body, gray plastic wheels ($150-200)
2. yellow body, black plastic wheels ($20-30)

6C EUCLID QUARRY TRUCK, issued 1964
1. yellow body, recessed rear tires ($8-12)
2. yellow body, solid rear tires ($8-12)

6D FORD PICKUP TRUCK, issued 1968
1. red body, white canopy, black plastic wheels, white grille ($8-12)
2. red body, white canopy, black plastic wheels, silver grille ($12-15)

7A HORSE DRAWN MILK FLOAT, issued 1954
1. orange body, silver painted bottle load, metal wheels ($125-150)
2. orange body, orange bottle load, metal wheels ($50-75)

3. orange body, orange bottle load, gray plastic wheels ($90-125)

7B FORD ANGLIA, issued 1961
1. light blue body, gray plastic wheels ($15-20)
2. light blue body, silver plastic wheels ($15-20)
3. light blue body, black plastic wheels ($12-15)

7C FORD REFUSE TRUCK, issued 1966
1. orange cab, silver metal loader, gray plastic dump ($5-8)

8A CATERPILLAR TRACTOR, issued 1955
1. orange body ($75-90)
2. light yellow body, red driver ($75-90)
3. dark yellow body ($25-30)

8B CATERPILLAR TRACTOR, issued 1959
1. yellow body, metal rollers, yellow driver ($45-60)

8C CATERPILLAR TRACTOR, issued 1961
1. yellow body, metal rollers ($45-55)
2. yellow body, silver plastic rollers ($60-75)
3. yellow body, black plastic rollers ($40-50)

8D CATERPILLAR TRACTOR, issued 1964
1. yellow body, black plastic rollers ($15-18)
2. yellow/orange body, black plastic rollers ($15-18)

8E FORD MUSTANG FASTBACK, issued 1966
1. white body, red interior, black plastic tires ($12-15)
2. orange body, red interior, black plastic tires ($90-125)

9A DENNIS FIRE ESCAPE, issued 1955
1. red body, no front bumper or number cast ($45-60)

9B DENNIS FIRE ESCAPE, issued 1957
1. red body, front bumper cast, no.9 cast, metal wheels ($45-60)
2. red body, front bumper cast, no.9 cast, gray plastic wheels ($125-150)

9C MERRYWEATHER MARQUIS FIRE ENGINE, issued 1959
1. red body, tan ladder, gray plastic wheels ($25-40)
2. red body, gold ladder, gray plastic wheels ($25-40)
3. red body, gold ladder, black plastic wheels ($12-15)
4. red body, silver ladder, black plastic wheels ($18-25)
5. red body, tan ladder, black plastic wheels ($18-25)

9D BOAT AND TRAILER, issued 1966
1. dull blue deck, white hull, dark blue trailer ($12-15)
2. bright blue deck, white hull, dark blue trailer ($5-8)

10A MECHANICAL HORSE & TRAILER, issued 1955
1. red cab, gray trailer, metal wheels ($25-35)

10B MECHANICAL HORSE & TRAILER, issued 1958
1. red cab, light tan trailer, metal wheels ($45-60)
2. red cab, dark tan trailer, gray plastic wheels ($50-60)

10C SUGAR CONTAINER TRUCK, issued 1961
1. dark blue body, crown decal on rear, gray plastic wheels ($50-75)
2. dark blue body, no crown decal on rear, gray plastic wheels ($25-40)
3. dark blue body, silver plastic wheels ($60-75)
4. dark blue body, black plastic wheels ($25-40)

10D PIPE TRUCK, issued 1966
1. red body, gray pipes, black plastic wheels, silver grille ($5-8)
2. red body, gray pipes, black plastic wheels, white grille ($10-15)

11A ROAD TANKER, issued 1955
1. green body, metal wheels ($250-500)
2. butterscotch yellow body, metal wheels ($75-90)
3. yellow body, metal wheels ($45-60)
4. red body, metal wheels, small "Esso" decal at rear ($25-40)
5. red body, metal wheels, large "Esso" decal at rear ($25-40)
6. dull red body, metal wheels, "Esso" decal at rear ($30-45)
7. red body, metal wheels, "Esso" decals on sides ($125-150)

11B ROAD TANKER, issued 1958
1. red body, "Esso" decals, gold trim, metal wheels ($35-50)
2. red body, "Esso" decals, silver trim, metal wheels ($25-40)
3. red body, "Esso" decals, gray plastic wheels ($25-40)
4. red body, "Esso" decals, silver plastic wheels ($150-175)
5. red body, "Esso" decals, black plastic wheels ($75-90)

11C JUMBO CRANE, issued 1965
1. yellow body, yellow weight box ($15-18)
2. yellow body, red weight box ($12-15)

11D SCAFFOLD TRUCK, issued 1969
1. silver-gray body, yellow scaffolding ($5-8)

12A LAND ROVER, issued 1955
1. olive green body ($25-40)

12B LAND ROVER, issued 1959
1. olive green body, gray plastic wheels ($75-90)
2. olive green body, black plastic wheels ($18-25)

12C SAFARI LAND ROVER, issued 1965
1. green body, brown luggage ($8-12)
2. blue body, brown luggage ($8-12)
3. blue body, tan luggage ($8-12)
4. gold body, tan luggage ($75-100)

13A BEDFORD WRECK TRUCK, issued 1955
1. tan body, red boom, metal wheels, no number cast ($35-50)

13B BEDFORD WRECK TRUCK, issued 1958
1. tan body, red boom, no. 13 cast, metal wheels ($35-50)
2. tan body, red boom, no. 13 cast, gray plastic wheels ($40-60)

13C THAMES WRECK TRUCK, issued 1961
1. red body, red metal hook, gray plastic wheels ($35-50)
2. red body, silver metal hook, gray plastic wheels ($35-50)

3. red body, silver metal hook, black plastic wheels ($25-40)
4. red body, gray plastic hook, black plastic wheels ($25-40)

13D DODGE WRECK TRUCK, issued 1965
1. green cab, yellow body, thin boom casting, gray hook, decals ($850-1000)
2. yellow cab, green body, gray hook, decals ($18-25)
3. yellow cab, green body, red hook, decals ($12-15)
4. yellow cab, green body, red hook, labels ($8-12)

* Note: models with green cab, yellow boom, thick boom casting, red hook and crimped axles were made in 1970 but were never issued ($600-800)

14A DAIMLER AMBULANCE, issued 1956
1. cream body, with red cross decal on roof, metal wheels ($25-40)
2. cream body, without red cross decal on roof, metal wheels ($25-40)

14B DAIMLER AMBULANCE, issued 1958
1. cream body, metal wheels ($25-40)
2. off white body, metal wheels ($25-40)
3. cream body, gray plastic wheels ($25-40)
4. off white body, gray plastic wheels ($25-40)
5. off white body, silver plastic wheels ($90-125)

14C BEDFORD AMBULANCE, issued 1962
1. white body, gray plastic wheels ($90-125)
2. white body, silver plastic wheels ($45-60)
3. white body, black plastic wheels ($15-18)

14D ISO GRIFO, issued 1968
1. dark blue body, black plastic tires ($5-8)

15A PRIME MOVER, issued 1956
1. yellow body, metal wheels ($500-750)
2. orange body, metal wheels ($20-30)
3. orange body, 10 gray plastic wheels ($175-200)

15B ATLANTIC PRIME MOVER, issued 1959
1. orange body, gray plastic wheels ($300-450)
2. orange body, black plastic wheels ($25-40)

15C REFUSE TRUCK, issued 1963
1. dark blue body, gray dump, decals, no peep hole cast ($35-50)
2. dark blue body, gray dump, decals ($12-15)
3. dark blue body, gray dump, labels ($12-15)

15D VOLKSWAGEN 1500 SALOON, issued 1968
1. off white body, "137" decals on doors ($8-12)
2. off white body, "137" labels on doors ($8-12)

16A ATLANTIC TRAILER, issued 1956
1. tan body, metal wheels ($25-40)

16B ATLANTIC TRAILER, issued 1957
1. tan body and towbar, gray plastic wheels ($35-50)
2. orange body, black towbar, gray plastic wheels ($90-125)
3. orange body, black towbar, black plastic wheels ($18-25)
4. orange body, unpainted towbar, black plastic wheels ($18-25)
5. orange body, orange towbar, black plastic wheels ($20-30)

16C SCAMMELL MOUNTAINEER SNOWPLOW, issued 1964
1. gray cab, orange dump, gray plastic wheels ($75-90)
2. gray cab, orange dump, black plastic wheels ($25-30)

16D CASE BULLDOZER, issued 1969
1. red body, yellow blade, green treads ($8-12)
2. bright red body, yellow blade, green treads ($8-12)
3. dark red body, yellow blade, black treads ($12-15)

17A BEDFORD REMOVALS VAN, issued 1956
1. maroon body, gold trim, metal wheels, no number cast ($150-175)
2. maroon body, silver trim, metal wheels, no number cast ($150-175)
3. blue body, metal wheels, no number cast ($150-175)

4. green body, metal wheels, no number cast, solid lettered decals ($25-40)
5. green body, metal wheels, no number cast, outlined decals ($35-50)

17B BEDFORD REMOVALS VAN, issued 1958
1. light green body, metal wheels, solid lettered decals, no.17 cast ($40-50)
2. light green body, metal wheels, outlined decals, no.17 cast ($50-75)
3. light green body, gray plastic wheels, outlined decals, no.17 cast ($50-75)
4. dark green body, gray plastic wheels, outlined decals no.17 cast ($50-75)

17C AUSTIN TAXI CAB, issued 1960
1. maroon body, light gray interior & base, gray plastic wheels ($35-50)
2. maroon body, light gray interior & base, silver plastic wheels ($50-75)
3. maroon body, dark gray interior & base, silver plastic wheels ($50-75)

17D HOVERINGHAM TIPPER, issued 1963
1. red cab, orange tipper, black baseplate ($12-15)
2. red cab, orange tipper, red baseplate ($12-15)

17E HORSE BOX, issued 1969
1. red cab, green plastic box, black plastic wheels ($5-8)

18A CATERPILLAR BULLDOZER, issued 1956
1. yellow body, red blade ($45-60)

18B CATERPILLAR BULLDOZER, issued 1958
1. yellow body & blade ($50-60)

18C CATERPILLAR BULLDOZER, issued 1961
1. yellow body & blade, metal rollers ($25-35)
2. yellow body & blade, silver plastic rollers ($75-90)
3. yellow body & blade, black plastic rollers ($25-30)

18D CATERPILLAR BULLDOZER, issued 1964
1. yellow body & blade, silver plastic rollers ($75-110)
2. yellow body & blade, black plastic rollers ($15-20)

18E FIELD CAR, issued 1969
1. yellow body, tan roof, black base, green wheels ($200-300)
2. yellow body, tan roof, unpainted base, green wheels ($200-300)
3. yellow body, tan roof, unpainted base, red wheels ($5-8)
4. yellow body, tan roof, black base, red wheels ($8-12)

19A MG SPORTS CAR, issued 1956
1. cream body, metal wheels ($45-60)
2. white body, metal wheels ($55-75)

19B MGA SPORTS CAR, issued 1958
1. white body, metal wheels, gold grille ($75-90)
2. white body, metal wheels, silver grille ($55-75)
3. white body, gray plastic wheels ($75-90)
4. white body, silver plastic wheels ($125-150)

19C ASTON MARTIN RACING CAR, issued 1961
1. metallic green body, gray driver, #52 decal ($35-50)
2. metallic green body, gray driver, #41 decal ($35-50)
3. metallic green body, gray driver, #5 decal ($35-50)
4. metallic green body, gray driver, #19 decal ($25-30)
5. metallic green body, white driver, #19 decal ($25-30)
6. metallic green body, white driver, #3 decal ($35-50)
7. metallic green body, white driver, $52 decal ($35-50)

19D LOTUS RACING CAR, issued 1966
1. orange body, black plastic tires, decals ($20-30)
2. orange body, black plastic tires, labels ($20-30)
3. green body, black plastic tires, decals ($15-20)
4. green body, black plastic tires, labels ($15-20)

20A STAKE TRUCK, issued 1956
1. maroon body, gold grille & tanks, metal wheels ($75-100)
2. maroon body, silver grille & tanks, metal wheels ($25-40)
3. maroon body, silver grille & tanks, gray plastic wheels ($85-110)
4. maroon body, maroon grille & tanks, metal wheels ($25-40)

5. dark red body, silver grille & tanks, metal wheels ($25-40)
6. dark red body, dk. red grille & tanks, gray plastic wheels ($85-100)

20B ERF 686 TRUCK, issued 1959
1. blue body, gray plastic wheels ($35-50)
2. blue body, silver plastic wheels ($75-90)
3. blue body, black plastic wheels ($35-50)

20C CHEVROLET IMPALA TAXI CAB, issued 1965
1. orange body, ivory interior, unpainted base, gray plastic wheels ($250-350)
2. orange body, ivory interior, silver/gray base, black plastic wheels ($18-25)
3. orange body, ivory interior, unpainted base, black plastic wheels ($8-12)
4. orange body, red interior, unpainted base, black plastic wheels ($8-12)
5. yellow body, red interior, unpainted base, black plastic wheels ($12-15)
6. yellow body, ivory interior, unpainted base, black plastic wheels ($12-15)

21A LONG DISTANCE COACH, issued 1956
1. light green body, metal wheels, "London to Glasgow" decals ($25-40)

21B LONG DISTANCE COACH, issued 1958
1. light green body, metal wheels, "London to Glasgow" decals ($35-50)
2. liqht green body, gray plastic wheels, "London to Glasgow" decals ($35-50)
3. dark green body, gray plastic wheels, "London to Glasgow" decals ($60-85)

21C COMMER MILK FLOAT, issued 1961
1. clear windows, silver plastic wheels, bottle decal, white load ($25-40)
2. clear windows, silver plastic wheels, bottle decal, cream load ($25-40)
3. green windows, silver plastic wheels, bottle decal, cream load ($25-40)
4. green windows, silver plastic wheels, bottle decal, white load ($25-40)
5. green windows, silver plastic wheels, cow decal, cream load ($25-40)
6. green windows, silver plastic wheels, cow decal, white load ($25-40)
7. green windows, gray plastic wheels, cow decal, cream load ($50-75)
8. green windows, black plastic wheels, cow decal, cream load ($15-18)
9. green windows, black plastic wheels, bottle decal, cream load ($15-18)

21D FODEN CONCRETE TRUCK, issued 1968
1. orange/yellow body and barrel, red chassis ($5-8)

22A VAUXHALL CRESTA, issued 1956
1. red body, cream roof, metal wheels ($25-40)
2. red body, white roof, metal wheels ($25-40)

22B 1958 VAUXHALL CRESTA, issued 1958
1. pinkish cream body, no windows, metal wheels ($35-50)
2. pinkish cream body, no windows, gray plastic wheels ($35-50)
3. pinkish cream body, green windows, gray plastic wheels ($45-50)
4. cream body, no windows, gray plastic wheels ($45-50)
5. pinkish cream body, green windows, gray plastic wheels ($35-50)
6. pinkish cream & turquoise body, green windows, gray plastic wheels ($300-450)
7. gun gray & turquoise body, green windows, gray plastic wheels ($60-75)
8. dull bronze & turquoise body, green windows, gray plastic wheels ($60-75)
9. bright bronze & turquoise body, green windows, gray plastic wheels ($60-75)
10. gray & pink body, green windows, gray plastic wheels ($45-60)
11. gray & pink body, green windows, silver plastic wheels ($45-60)
12. gold body, green windows, gray plastic wheels ($45-60)
13. gold body, green windows, silver plastic wheels ($45-60)
14. copper body, green windows, gray plastic wheels ($45-60)
15. copper body, green windows, silver plastic wheels ($45-60)
16. copper body, green windows, black plastic wheels ($35-45)

22C PONTIAC GRAN PRIX SPORTS COUPE, issued 1964
1. orange/red body, black plastic wheels ($12-15)
2. red body, black plastic wheels ($12-15)

23A BERKELEY CAVALIER TRAILER, issued 1956
1. pale blue body, metal whls., faint door outline, no number cast ($25-40)

23B BERKELEY CAVALIER TRAILER, issued 1958
1. pale blue body, metal wheels, heavy door outline, no.23 cast ($25-40)
2. lime green body, metal wheels ($35-50)
3. lime green body, gray plastic wheels ($35-50)
4. metallic green body, gray plastic wheels ($250-350)

23C BLUEBIRD DAUPHINE TRAILER, issued 1960
1. metallic green body, gray plastic wheels ($250-350)
2. metallic tan body, gray plastic wheels ($45-60)
3. metallic tan body, silver plastic wheels ($45-60)
4. metallic tan body, black plastic wheels ($75-100)

23D TRAILER CARAVAN, issued 1965
1. yellow body, white roof, black plastic wheels ($12-15)
2. pink body, white roof, black plastic wheels ($12-15)

24A WEATHERHILL HYDRAULIC EXCAVATOR, issued 1956
1. orange body, metal wheels ($25-40)
2. yellow body, metal wheels ($25-40)

24B WEATHERHILL HYDRAULIC EXCAVATOR, issued 1959
1. yellow body, gray plastic wheels ($25-35)
2. yellow body, black plastic wheels ($20-30)

24C ROLLS ROYCE SILVER SHADOW, issued 1967
1. metallic red body, black plastic tires ($5-8)

25A DUNLOP VAN, issued 1956
1. dark blue body, "Dunlop" decals, metal wheels ($25-40)
2. dark blue body, "Dunlop" decals, gray plastic wheels ($25-40)

25B VOLKSWAGEN 1200 SEDAN, issued 1960
1. silver blue body, clear windows, gray plastic wheels ($35-50)
2. silver blue body, green windows, gray plastic wheels ($35-50)
3. silver blue body, green windows, silver gray wheels ($50-65)
4. silver blue body, green windows, black plastic wheels ($100-125)

25C PETROL TANKER, issued 1964
1. yellow cab, green chassis, "BP" decals, gray plastic wheels ($125-150)
2. yellow cab, green chassis, "BP" decals, black plastic wheels ($15-18)
3. dark blue cab & chassis, "Aral" decals, black plastic wheels ($75-90)

25D FORD CORTINA, issued 1968
1. light brown body, black plastic wheels, no roof rack ($5-8)
2. light brown body, black plastic wheels, yellow roof rack ($8-12)

26A CONCRETE TRUCK, issued 1956
1. orange body, metal wheels, gold grille ($75-90)
2. orange body, metal wheels, silver grille ($25-40)
3. orange body, gray plastic wheels ($45-60)
4. orange body, silver plastic wheels ($125-150)

26B FODEN CONCRETE TRUCK, issued 1961
1. orange body, gray barrel, gray plastic wheels ($300-450)
2. orange body & barrel, gray plastic wheels ($25-40)
3. orange body & barrel, silver plastic wheels ($125-150)
4. orange body & barrel, black plastic wheels ($15-18)

26C G.M.C. TIPPER TRUCK, issued 1968
1. red cab, green chassis, silver dump, black plastic wheels ($5-8)

27A BEDFORD LOWLOADER, issued 1956
1. light blue cab, dark blue trailer, metal wheels ($500-750)
2. dark green cab, tan trailer, metal wheels ($25-40)

27B BEDFORD LOWLOADER, issued 1959
1. light green cab, tan trailer, metal wheels ($35-50)
2. light green cab, tan trailer, gray plastic wheels ($50-75)
3. dark green cab, tan trailer, gray plastic wheels ($65-90)

27C CADILLAC SIXTY SPECIAL, issued 1960
1. green body, silver plastic wheels, red base, clear windows ($250-350)
2. silver-gray body, white roof, silver wheels, red base, clear windows ($25-40)

3. silver-gray body, pink roof, silver wheels, red base, clear windows ($25-40)
4. silver-gray body, pink roof, silver wheels, red base, green windows ($25-40)
5. lilac body, pink roof, silver wheels, red base, green windows ($25-40)
6. lilac body, pink roof, silver wheels, black base, green windows ($25-40)
7. lilac body, pink roof, gray wheels, black base, green windows ($25-40)
8. lilac body, pink roof, black wheels, black base, green windows ($25-40)

27D MERCEDES BENZ 230SL, issued 1966
1. cream body, black plastic wheels ($5-8)
2. white body, black plastic wheels ($7-10)

28A BEDFORD COMPRESSOR TRUCK, issued 1956
1. orange body, metal wheels ($25-40) body, metal wheels ($25-40)
2. yellow body, gray plastic wheels ($150-175) body, black plastic wheels ($25-35)

28B THAMES COMPRESSOR TRUCK, issued 1959
1. yellow body, gray plastic wheels ($150-175)
2. yellow body, black plastic wheels ($25-35)

28C MK.10 JAGUAR, issued 1964
1. light brown body & motor, gray plastic wheels ($125-150)
2. light brown body & motor, black plastic wheels ($15-18)
3. light brown body, unpainted motor, black plastic wheels ($15-18)

28D MACK DUMP TRUCK, issued 1968
1. orange body, red plastic wheels with black tires ($8-12)
2. orange body, yellow plastic wheels with black tires ($8-12)

29A BEDFORD MILK DELIVERY VAN, issued 1956
1. tan body, metal wheels ($25-40)
2. tan body, gray plastic wheels ($35-50)

29B AUSTIN A55 CAMBRIDGE SEDAN, issued 1961
1. two-tone green body, gray plastic wheels ($35-40)

2. two-tone green body, silver plastic wheels ($20-25)
3. two-tone green body, black plastic wheels ($20-25)

29C FIRE PUMPER, issued 1966
1. red body, "Denver" decals, black plastic wheels ($8-12)
2. red body, shield label, black plastic wheels ($8-12)
3. red body, no labels, black plastic wheels ($7-10)

30A FORD PREFECT, issued 1956
1. light blue body, metal wheels ($90-125)
2. light blue body, gray plastic wheels ($90-125)
3. gray-brown body, metal wheels ($25-40)
4. olive brown body, gray plastic wheels ($35-50)

30B MAGIRUZ-DEUTZ 6-WHEEL CRANE TRUCK, issued 1961
1. tan body, red boom, gray plastic wheels ($750-850)
2. tan body, orange boom, gray plastic wheels ($750-850)
3. silver body, orange boom, gray plastic wheels, orange metal hook ($35-50)
4. silver body, orange boom, gray plastic whls., silver metal hook ($35-50)
5. silver body, orange boom, silver plastic wheels, silver metal hook ($35-50)
6. silver body, orange boom, black plastic whls., silver metal hook ($25-40)
7. silver body, orange boom, black plastic whls., gray plastic hook ($25-40)

30C 8-WHEEL CRANE TRUCK, issued 1965
1. mint green body, orange boom, black plastic wheels ($850-1000)
2. dark green body, orange boom, black plastic wheels ($5-8)

31A FORD STATION WAGON, issued 1957
1. yellow body, metal wheels ($30-40)
2. yellow body, gray plastic wheels ($35-50)

31B FORD FAIRLANE STATION WAGON, issued 1960
1. yellow body, red base, clear windows, silver plastic wheels ($90-125)
2. yellow body, black base, clear windows, silver plastic wheels ($90-125)
3. green w/pink roof, red base, clear windows, silver plastic whls. ($35-50)

4. green w/pink roof, red base, green windows, silver plastic whls. ($35-50)
5. green w/pink roof, black base, green windows, silver plastic wheels ($35-50)
6. green w/pink roof, black base, green windows, gray plastic wheels ($45-60)
7. green w/pink roof, black base, green windows, black plastic wheels ($90-125)

31C LINCOLN CONTINENTAL, issued 1964
1. metallic blue body, black plastic wheels ($7-10)
2. mint green body, black plastic wheels ($5-8)
3. metallic lime body, black plastic wheels ($450-600)

32A JAGUAR XK140 COUPE, issued 1957
1. cream body, metal wheels ($25-40)
2. cream body, gray plastic wheels ($25-40)
3. red body, gray plastic wheels ($85-100)

32B JAGUAR XKE, issued 1962
1. metallic red body, clear windows, gray plastic tires ($35-50)
2. metallic red body, green windows, gray plastic tires ($20-30)
3. metallic red body, clear windows, black plastic tires ($20-30)
4. metallic bronze body, clear windows, black plastic tires ($35-50)

32C LEYLAND PETROL TANKER, issued 1968
1. green cab & chassis, "BP" labels, silver grille ($5-8)
2. green cab & chassis, "BP" labels, white grille ($8-12)
3. dark blue cab & chassis, "Aral" labels, silver grille ($35-50)

33A FORD ZODIAC MKII SEDAN, issued 1957
1. light blue body, no windows, metal wheels ($25-40)
2. light blue-green body, no windows, metal wheels ($25-40)
3. dark green body, no windows, metal wheels ($35-50)
4. dark green body, no windows, gray plastic wheels ($35-50)
5. silver-gray & orange body, no windows, gray plastic wheels ($45-60)
6. tan & light orange, no windows, gray plastic wheels ($35-50)

7. tan & orange body, no windows, gray plastic wheels ($35-50)
8. tan & orange body, green windows, gray plastic wheels ($35-50)
9. tan & orange body, green windows, silver plastic wheels ($35-50)

33B FORD ZEPHYR 6 MK III, issued 1963
1. blue-green body, gray plastic wheels ($20-35)
2. blue-green body, silver plastic wheels ($25-40)
3. blue-green body, black plastic wheels ($15-18)
4. light blue-green body, black plastic wheels ($15-18)

33C LAMBORGHINI MIURA, issued 1969
1. yellow body, ivory interior, black plastic tires ($50-75)
2. yellow body, red interior, black plastic tires ($5-8)
3. gold body, ivory interior, black plastic tires ($50-75)

34A VOLKSWAGEN MICROVAN, issued 1957
1. blue body, metal wheels ($25-40)
2. blue body, gray plastic wheels ($35-50)
3. blue body, silver plastic wheels ($75-100)
4. blue body, black plastic wheels ($125-150)

34B VOLKSWAGEN CAMPER, issued 1962
1. light green body, gray plastic wheels ($35-50)
2. light green body, black plastic wheels ($35-50)

34C VOLKSWAGEN CAMPER, issued 1967
1. silver body, raised roof with six windows ($8-12)

34D VOLKSWAGEN CAMPER, issued 1968
1. silver body, short raised roof without windows ($7-10)

35A MARSHALL HORSE BOX, issued 1957
1. red cab, brown box, metal wheels ($25-40)
2. red cab, brown box, gray plastic wheels ($35-50)
3. red cab, brown box, silver plastic wheels ($75-90)
4. red cab, brown box, black plastic wheels ($50-75)

35B SNOW TRAC TRACTOR, issued 1964
1. red body, white treads, "Snow Trac" decals ($18-25)
2. red body, white treads, plain sides ($18-25)
3. red body, white treads "Snow Trac" cast on sides ($18-25)
4. red body, gray treads, "Snow Trac" cast on sides ($25-40)

36A AUSTIN A50, issued 1957
1. blue-green body, metal wheels ($25-40)
2. blue-green body, gray plastic wheels ($25-40)

36B LAMBRETTA SCOOTER & SIDECAR, issued 1961
1. dark metallic green, black plastic wheels ($50-75)
2. light metallic green, black plastic wheels ($50-75)

36C OPEL DIPLOMAT, issued 1966
1. gold body, silver plastic motor, black plastic wheels ($5-8)
2. gold body, gray plastic motor, black plastic wheels ($8-10)
3. sea green body, gray plastic motor & base, black plastic wheels ($650-800)

37A COCA COLA LORRY, issued 1956
1. orange body, no baseplate, uneven cast case load, metal wheels ($85-100)
2. orange body, no baseplate, even cast case load, metal wheels ($45-60)
3. orange body, no baseplate, even cast case load, gray plastic wheels ($45-60)

37B COCA COLA LORRY, issued 1960
1. yellow body, black baseplate, gray plastic wheels ($45-60)
2. yellow body, black baseplate, silver plastic wheels ($125-150)
3. yellow body, black baseplate, black plastic wheels ($45-60)

37C DODGE CATTLE TRUCK, issued 1966
1. yellow body, gray box, silver plastic baseplate ($8-12)
2. yellow body, gray box, unpainted metal baseplate ($5-8)

38A KARRIER REFUSE COLLECTOR, issued 1957
1. gray-brown body, metal wheels ($90-125)
2. dark gray body, metal wheels ($25-40)
3. dark gray body, gray plastic wheels ($25-40)
4. silver body, gray plastic wheels ($35-50)

38B VAUXHALL VICTOR ESTATE CAR, issued 1963
1. yellow body, green interior, gray plastic wheels ($25-35)
2. yellow body, green interior, silver plastic wheels ($25-40)
3. yellow body, green interior, black plastic wheels ($20-30)
4. yellow body, red interior, silver plastic wheels ($20-30)
5. yellow body, red interior, black plastic wheels ($20-30)

38C HONDA MOTORCYCLE & TRAILER, issued 1967
1. blue-green cycle, orange trailer, no decals, black plastic wheels ($18-25)
2. blue-green cycle, orange trailer, "Honda" decal, black plastic wheels ($20-35)
3. blue-green cycle, yellow trailer, "Honda" decal, black plastic wheels ($8-12)
4. blue-green cycle, yellow trailer, "Honda" label, black plastic wheels ($8-12)

39A FORD ZODIAC CONVERTIBLE, issued 1957
1. pink body, tan interior & base, metal wheels ($90-125)
2. pink body, turquoise interior & base, metal wheels ($25-40)
3. pink body, turquoise interior & base, gray plastic wheels ($35-50)
4. pink body, turquoise interior & base, silver plastic wheels ($50-75)

*NOTE: pink bodies vary in shades from light to dark pink

39B PONTIAC CONVERTIBLE, issued 1962
1. purple body, red steering wheel, red base, silver plastic wheels ($75-90)
2. purple body, red steering wheel, red base, gray plastic wheels ($85-100)
3. yellow body, red steering wheel, red base, silver plastic wheels ($25-40)
4. yellow body, red steering wheel, red base, gray plastic wheels ($25-40)
5. yellow body, ivory steering wheel, red base, silver plastic wheels ($20-30)

6. yellow body, ivory steering wheel, red base, gray plastic whls ($20-30)
7. yellow body, ivory steering wheel, black base, silver plastic wheels ($20-30)
8. yellow body, ivory steering wheel, black base, gray plastic wheels ($20-30)
9. yellow body, ivory steering wheel, black base, black plastic wheels ($20-30)

39C FORD TRACTOR, issued 1967
1. dark blue body, yellow hood, black plastic tires ($8-12)
2. dark blue body & hood, black plastic tires ($8-12)
3. light blue body & hood, black plastic tires ($8-12)

*Note: orange body version issued in 1970- to be listed in book #2

40A BEDFORD TIPPER TRUCK, issued 1957
1. red cab & chassis, tan dump, metal wheels ($25-40)
2. red cab & chassis, tan dump, gray plastic wheels ($25-40)
3. red cab & chassis, dark tan dump, gray plastic wheels ($25-40)

40B LEYLAND ROYAL TIGER COACH, issued 1961
1. silver/gray body, gray plastic wheels ($25-40)
2. silver/gray body, silver plastic wheels ($20-30)
3. silver/gray body, black plastic wheels ($18-25)

40C HAY TRAILER, issued 1967
1. blue body, yellow stakes, black plastic tires ($5-8)

41A D-TYPE JAGUAR, issued 1957
1. green body, metal wheels, "41" decal ($25-40)
2. green body, gray plastic wheels, "41" decal ($35-50)

41B D-TYPE JAGUAR, issued 1960
1. green body, gray plastic wheels, "41" decal ($35-50)
2. green body, silver plastic wheels, "19" decal ($125-150)
3. green body, black plastic tires & spoked wheels, "41" decal ($35-50)
4. green body, black plastic tires & spoked wheels, "5" decal ($45-60)

5. green body, black plastic tires & red wheels, "41" decal ($175-200)

41C FORD GT, issued 1965
1. white body, black plastic tires, red wheels, "6" decal ($90-125)
2. white body, black plastic tires, yellow wheels, "6" decal ($7-10)
3. white body, black plastic tires, yellow wheels, "9" decal ($12-15)
4. yellow body, black plastic tires, yellow wheels, "6" decal ($50-75)
5. white body, black plastic tires, yellow wheels, "6" label ($7-10)
6. white body, black plastic tires, yellow wheels, "9" label ($7-10)

42A BEDFORD EVENING NEWS VAN, issued 1957
1. yellow-orange body, metal wheels ($35-50)
2. yellow-orange body, gray plastic wheels ($35-50)
3. yellow-orange body, black plastic wheels ($35-50)

42B STUDEBAKER LARK WAGONAIRE, issued 1965
1. blue body, blue rear sliding roof, black plastic wheels ($12-15)
2. blue body, light blue rear sliding roof, black plastic wheels ($10-15)

42C IRON FAIRY CRANE, issued 1969
1. red body, orange-yellow boom, black plastic wheels ($5-8)

43A HILLMAN MINX, issued 1958
1. green body, metal wheels ($175-225)
2. bluish gray body with gray roof, metal wheels ($35-50)
3. bluish gray body with gray roof, gray plastic wheels ($35-50)
4. turquoise body with cream roof, gray plastic wheels ($25-40)

43B AVELING BARFORD TRACTOR SHOVEL, issued 1962
1. yellow body, yellow shovel, yellow base, yellow driver ($35-50)
2. yellow body, yellow shovel, red base, red driver ($25-35)
3. yellow body, red shovel, yellow base, yellow driver ($25-35)
4. yellow body, red shovel, red base, red driver ($35-50)

43C PONY TRAILER, issued 1968
1. yellow body, tan baseplate, black plastic wheels ($5-8)
2. yellow body, dark green baseplate, black plastic wheels ($5-8)

44A ROLLS ROYCE SILVER CLOUD, issued 1958
1. metallic blue, metal wheels ($25-40)
2. metallic blue, gray plastic wheels ($35-50)
3. metallic blue, silver plastic wheels ($35-50)

44B ROLLS ROYCE PHANTOM V, issued 1964
1. metallic tan body, gray plastic wheels ($75-100)
2. metallic gray body, black plastic wheels ($25-40)
3. metallic silver/gray body, black plastic wheels ($25-40)
4. metallic tan body, black plastic wheels ($15-20)

44C G.M.C. REFRIGERATOR TRUCK, issued 1967
1. red cab & chassis, turquoise container, black plastic wheels ($5-8)

45A VAUXHALL VICTOR, issued 1958
1. red body, no windows, metal wheels ($850-1000)
2. yellow body, no windows, metal wheels ($25-40)
3. yellow body, no windows, gray plastic wheels ($25-40)
4. yellow body, green windows, gray plastic wheels ($25-40)
5. yellow body, clear windows, gray plastic wheels ($25-40)
6. yellow body, green windows, silver plastic wheels ($35-50)
7. yellow body, green windows, black plastic wheels ($20-30)

45B FORD CORSAIR WITH BOAT, issued 1965
1. pale yellow body, gray plastic wheels, unpainted baseplate ($25-40)
2. pale yellow body, black plastic wheels, unpainted baseplate ($12-15)
3. Pale yellow body, black plastic wheels, silver-gray baseplate ($15-18)

46A MORRIS MINOR 1000, issued 1958
1. light tan body, metal wheels ($750-900)
2. dark green body, metal wheels ($50-65)
3. dark green body, gray plastic wheels ($50-75)
4. dark blue body, gray plastic wheels ($75-90)

46B PICKFORDS REMOVAL VAN, issued 1960
1. dark blue body, 2 line "Pickfords" decal, gray plastic wheels ($60-75)
2. dark blue body, 2 line "Pickfords" decal, silver plastic wheels ($90-110)

3. dark blue body, 3 line "Pickfords" decal, gray plastic wheels ($60-75)
4. dark blue body, 3 line "Pickfords" decal, silver plastic wheels ($75-90)
5. green body, 3 line "Pickfords" decal, gray plastic wheels ($40-50)
6. green body, 3 line "Pickfords" decal, silver plastic wheels ($75-90)
7. green body, 3 line "Pickfords" decal, black plastic wheels ($18-25)
8. green body, 2 line "Pickfords" decal, black plastic wheels ($90-125)
9. tan body, "Beales Bealson" decal, black plastic wheels ($275-325)

46C MERCEDES BENZ 300 SE, issued 1968
1. green body, black plastic wheels ($8-12)
2. blue body, black plastic wheels ($7-10)

47A 1 TON TROJAN VAN, issued 1958
1. red body, "Brooke Bond" decals, metal wheels ($25-40)
2. red body, "Brooke Bond" decals, gray plastic wheels ($35-50)

47B COMMER ICE CREAM CANTEEN, issued 1963
1. blue body, squared roof decal, striped side decal, gray plastic wheels ($150-175)
2. blue body, squared roof decal, striped side decal, black plastic wheels ($20-35)
3. blue body, oval roof decal, plain side decal, black plastic wheels ($20-35)
4. met. blue body, squared roof decal, striped side decal, black plastic wheels ($90-125)
5. cream body, squared roof decal, striped side decal, black plastic wheels ($50-75)
6. cream body, oval roof decal, plain side decal, black plastic wheels ($35-50)

47C DAF TIPPER CONTAINER TRUCK, issued 1968
1. aqua blue cab & chassis, yellow container, light gray roof ($20-30)
2. silver cab & chassis, yellow container, light gray roof ($5-8)
3. silver cab & chassis, yellow container, dark gray roof ($5-8)

48A METEOR SPORTS BOAT & TRAILER, issued 1958
1. tan deck, blue hull, black trailer, metal wheels ($25-40)

2. tan deck, blue hull, black trailer, gray plastic wheels ($45-60)
3. tan deck, blue hull, black trailer, silver plastic wheels ($75-90)

48B SPORTS BOAT & TRAILER, issued 1961
1. white deck, red hull, silver motor, dark blue trailer, gray plastic wheels ($50-75)
2. white deck, red hull, silver motor, dark blue trailer, black plastic wheels ($25-40)
3. white deck, red hull, gold motor, dark blue trailer, black plastic wheels ($20-30)
4. white deck, red hull, gold motor, light blue trailer, black plastic wheels ($20-30)
5. red deck, white hull, silver motor, dark blue trailer, black plastic wheels ($25-40)
6. red deck, white hull, gold motor, dark blue trailer, black plastic wheels ($20-30)
7. red deck, white hull, gold motor, light blue trailer, black plastic wheels ($20-30)

48C DODGE DUMPER TRUCK, issued 1966
1. red body, black plastic wheels, base runs full length ($5-8)
2. red body, black plastic wheels, base runs three-quarter length ($5-8)

49A M3 PERSONNEL CARRIER, issued 1958
1. olive body, metal front wheels, metal rollers ($20-30)
2. olive body, gray plastic front wheels, metal rollers ($25-40)
3. olive body, gray plastic front wheels, gray plastic rollers ($75-90)
4. olive body, gray plastic front wheels, silver plastic rollers ($60-75)
5. olive body, black plastic front wheels, black plastic rollers ($18-25)

49B MERCEDES UNIMOG, issued 1967
1. tan cab & bed, turquoise chassis & baseplate, black plastic tires ($8-12)
2. blue cab & bed, red chassis & baseplate, black plastic tires ($7-10)

50A COMMER PICKUP, issued 1958
1. dark tan body, metal wheels ($25-40)
2. light tan body, metal wheels ($25-40)
3. light tan body, gray plastic wheels ($25-40)
4. dark tan body, gray plastic wheels ($25-40)
5. dark tan body, silver plastic wheels ($75-90)
6. red and white body, silver plastic wheels ($250-300)
7. red and gray body, silver plastic wheels ($75-100)
8. red and gray body, gray plastic wheels ($50-75)
9. red and gray body, black plastic wheels ($50-75)

50B JOHN DEERE TRACTOR, issued 1964
1. green body, gray plastic tires ($20-30)
2. green body, black plastic tires ($18-25)

50C FORD KENNEL TRUCK, issued 1969
1. green body, tinted canopy, white grille ($5-8)
2. green body, clear canopy, white grille ($5-8)
3. green body, clear canopy, silver grille ($5-8)
4. green body, tinted canopy, silver grille ($5-8)

51A ALBION CHIEFTAN, issued 1958
1. yellow body, "Portland Cement" decals, metal wheels ($25-40)
2. yellow body, "Blue Circle Portland Cement" decals, metal whls ($25-40)
3. yellow body, "Blue Circle Portland Cement" decals, gray plastic wheels ($25-40)
4. yellow body, "Blue Circle Portland Cement" decals, silver plastic wheels ($50-75)
5. yellow body, "Blue Circle Portland Cement" decals, black plastic wheels ($75-90)

51B JOHN DEERE TRAILER, issued 1964
1. green body and towbar, gray plastic tires ($20-30)
2. green body and towbar, black plastic tires ($18-25)

51C 8-WHEEL TIPPER, issued 1969
1. orange cab, white grille, "Douglas" labels, black plastic wheels ($18-25)
2. orange cab, silver grille, "Douglas" labels, black plastic wheels ($10-15)
3. yellow cab, silver grille, "Douglas" labels, black plastic wheels ($10-15)
4. yellow cab, silver grille, "Pointer" labels, black plastic wheels ($7-10)

52A MASERATI 4CLT RACER, issued 1958
1. red body, black plastic wheels, no decals ($35-50)
2. red body, black plastic wheels, "52" decal ($45-60)
3. red body, black plastic tires with spoked wheels, no decals ($90-125)
4. yellow body, black plastic tires with spoked wheels, "5" decal ($50-75)
5. yellow body, black plastic tires with spoked wheels, "52" decal ($40-50)
6. yellow body, black plastic tires with spoked wheels, "3" decal ($50-75)

52B BRM RACING CAR, issued 1965
1. blue body, "5" decal, black plastic tires ($7-10)
2. blue body, "3" decal, black plastic tires ($35-50)
3. blue body, "5" label, black plastic tires ($7-10)
4. red body, "5" decal, black plastic tires ($18-25)
5. red body, "5" label, black plastic tires ($18-25)

53A ASTON MARTIN, issued 1958
1. metallic light green, metal wheels ($25-40)
2. metallic light green, gray plastic wheels ($25-40)
3. metallic red, gray plastic wheels ($125-150)
4. metallic red, black plastic wheels ($90-110)

53B MERCEDES BENZ 220SE, issued 1963
1. maroon body, gray plastic wheels ($20-30)
2. maroon body, silver plastic wheels ($25-40)
3. maroon body, black plastic wheels ($35-50)
4. red body, gray plastic wheels ($20-30)
5. red body, black plastic wheels ($18-25)

53C FORD ZODIAC MK IV, issued 1968
1. metallic silver blue body, black plastic wheels ($5-8)
2. light metallic green body, black plastic wheels ($500-650)

54A SARACEN PERSONNEL CARRIER, issued 1958
1. olive body, black plastic wheels ($12-15)

54B S & S CADILLAC AMBULANCE, issued 1965
1. white body, cross decal, black plastic wheels ($7-10)

2. white body, cross label, black plastic wheels ($7-10)

55A D.U.K.W., issued 1958
1. olive body, metal wheels ($25-40)
2. olive body, gray plastic wheels ($25-40)
3. olive body, black plastic wheels ($25-40)

55B FORD FAIRLANE POLICE CAR, issued 1963
1. dark blue body, black plastic wheels ($175-200)
2. light blue body, gray plastic wheels ($75-100)
3. light blue body, silver plastic wheels ($75-100)
4. light blue body, black plastic wheels ($25-40)

55C FORD GALAXIE POLICE CAR, issued 1966
1. white body, blue dome light, decals, black plastic wheels ($45-60)
2. white body, red dome light, decals, black plastic wheels ($15-20)
3. white body, red dome light, labels, black plastic wheels ($15-20)

55D MERCURY POLICE CAR, issued 1968
1. white body, black plastic tires, red dome light ($45-60)
2. white body, black plastic tires, blue dome light ($7-10)

56A LONDON TROLLEY BUS, issued 1958
1. red body, black trolley poles, metal wheels ($175-200)
2. red body, red trolley poles, metal wheels ($25-40)
3. red body, red trolley poles, gray plastic wheels ($35-50)
4. red body, red trolley poles, silver plastic wheels ($75-90)
5. red body, red trolley poles, black plastic wheels ($45-60)

56B FIAT 1500, issued 1965
1. turquoise body, brown luggage, black plastic wheels ($8-12)
2. turquoise body, tan luggage, black plastic wheels ($8-12)
3. red body, tan luggage, black plastic wheels ($75-90)

57A WOLSELEY 1500, issued 1958
1. pale yellow-green body, gold grille, gray plastic wheels ($50-75)
2. pale yellow-green body, silver grille, gray plastic wheels ($25-40)

3. pale green body, silver grille, gray plastic wheels ($25-40)
4. pale gray body, silver grille, gray plastic wheels ($100-125)

57B CHEVROLET IMPALA, issued 1961
1. met. blue with blue roof, black base, gray plastic wheels ($25-40)
2. met. blue with blue roof, black base, silver plastic wheels ($25-40)
3. met. blue with blue roof, dark blue base, silver plastic wheels ($25-40)
4. met. blue with blue roof, light blue base, silver plastic wheels ($25-40)
5. met. blue with blue roof, black base, black plastic wheels ($25-40)

57C LAND ROVER FIRE TRUCK, issued 1966
1. red body, gray plastic wheels, decals ($175-200)
2. red body, black plastic wheels, decals ($8-12)
3. red body, black plastic wheels, labels ($8-12)

58A BEA COACH, issued 1958
1. blue body, "British European Airways" decals, gray plastic wheels ($25-40)
2. blue body, "BEA" decals, gray plastic wheels ($30-45)
3. blue body, "BEA" decals, silver plastic wheels ($75-100)
4. blue body, "BEA" decals, black plastic wheels ($75-100)

58B DROTT EXCAVATOR, issued 1962
1. red body, silver motor & baseplate, metal rollers ($20-35)
2. red body, silver motor & baseplate, silver plastic rollers ($75-100)
3. red body, silver motor & baseplate, black plastic rollers ($20-35)
4. orange body, silver motor & baseplate, black plastic rollers ($25-40)
5. orange body, orange motor & baseplate, black plastic rollers ($25-40)

58C DAF GIRDER TRUCK, issued 1968
1. cream body, red plastic girders ($5-8)

59A FORD THAMES VAN, issued 1958
1. light green body, gray plastic wheels ($25-40)
2. light green body, silver plastic wheels ($75-90)
3. dark kelly green, gray plastic wheels ($90-110)
4. dark kelly green, silver plastic wheels ($100-125)

59B FORD FAIRLANE FIRE CHIEF CAR, issued 1963
1. red body, gray plastic wheels ($75-100)
2. red body, silver plastic wheels ($125-150)
3. red body, black plastic wheels ($18-25)

59C FORD GALAXIE FIRE CHIEF CAR, issued 1966
1. red body, decal on hood and sides, black plastic wheels ($8-12)
2. red body, decal on hood, label on sides, black plastic wheels ($8-12)
3. red body, label on hood and sides, black plastic wheels ($8-12)

60A MORRIS J2 PICKUP, issued 1958
1. blue body, red & black decal, with rear window cast, gray plastic wheels ($25-40)
2. blue body, red & black decal, with rear window cast, silver plastic wheels ($35-50)
3. blue body, red & white decal, with rear window cast, gray plastic wheels ($25-40)
4. blue body, red & white decal, with rear window cast, silver plastic wheels ($35-50)
5. blue body, red & white decal, with rear window cast, black plastic wheels ($25-40)
6. blue body, red & white decal, no rear window cast, black plastic wheels ($25-40)

60B SITE HUT TRUCK, issued 1966
1. blue body, yellow plastic hut with green roof, black plastic wheels ($5-8)

61A FERRET SCOUT CAR, issued 1959
1. olive green body, black plastic wheels ($12-18)

61B ALVIS STALWART, issued 1966
1. white body, yellow roof, green wheels, decals ($7-10)
2. white body, yellow roof, green wheels, labels ($7-10)
3. white body, yellow roof, yellow wheels, labels ($25-35)

62A GENERAL SERVICE LORRY, issued 1959
1. olive green body, black plastic tires ($35-50)

62B TV SERVICE VAN, issued 1963
1. cream body, gray plastic wheels, "Rentaset" decals ($125-150)
2. cream body, black plastic wheels, "Rentaset" decals ($20-35)
3. cream body, gray plastic wheels, "Radio Rentals" decals ($150-200)
4. cream body, black plastic wheels, "Radio Rentals" decals ($35-50)

62C MERCURY COUGAR, issued 1968
1. pale yellow body, black plastic tires ($700-850)
2. metallic lime green body, black plastic tires ($5-8)

63A FORD SERVICE AMBULANCE, issued 1959
1. olive green body, black plastic wheels ($35-50)

63B FOAMITE CRASH TENDER, issued 1964
1. red body, silver nozzle, black plastic wheels ($25-40)
2. red body, gold nozzle, black plastic wheels ($18-25)

63C DODGE CRANE TRUCK, issued 1968
1. yellow body, red hook, black plastic wheels ($5-8)
2. yellow body, yellow hook, black plastic wheels ($7-10)

64A SCAMMELL BREAKDOWN TRUCK, issued 1959
1. olive green body, green metal hook, black plastic wheels ($25-40)
2. olive green body, silver metal hook, black plastic wheels ($25-40)
3. olive green body, gray plastic hook, black plastic wheels ($25-40)

64B MG1100, issued 1966
1. green body, black plastic wheels ($7-10)

65A JAGUAR 3.4 LITRE SALOON, issued 1959
1. metallic blue body, gray plastic wheels ($25-40)
2. blue body, gray plastic wheels ($25-40)

65B JAGUAR 3.4 LITRE SALOON, issued 1962
1. red body, gray plastic wheels ($25-40)
2. red body, silver plastic wheels ($35-50)

3. metallic red body, silver plastic wheels ($35-50)
4. red body, black plastic wheels ($20-30)

65C CLAAS COMBINE HARVESTER, issued 1967
1. red body, yellow rotating blades, black plastic wheels ($5-8)

66A CITROEN DS19, issued 1959
1. yellow body, gray plastic wheels ($45-60)
2. yellow body, silver plastic wheels ($100-125)

66B HARLEY DAVIDSON MOTORCYCLE & SIDECAR, issued 1962
1. metallic bronze body, black plastic tires ($75-90)

66C GREYHOUND BUS, issued 1967
1. silver-gray body, blue decal, clear windows ($50-75)
2. silver-gray body, blue decal, amber windows ($7-10)
3. silver-gray body, gray label, amber windows ($7-10)

67A SALADIN ARMOURED CAR, issued 1959
1. olive body, black plastic wheels ($15-18)

67B VOLKSWAGEN 1600TL, issued 1967
1. red body, no roof rack, black plastic tires ($5-8)
2. red body, maroon roof rack, black plastic tires ($10-15)
3. purple body, no roof rack, black plastic tires ($90-110)

68A AUSTIN MKII RADIO TRUCK, issued 1959
1. olive body, black plastic wheels ($30-45)

68B MERCEDES COACH, issued 1965
1. turquoise body, white roof, black plastic wheels ($50-75)
2. orange body, white roof, black plastic wheels ($7-10)

69A COMMER 30 CWT VAN, issued 1959
1. maroon body, gray plastic wheels ($25-40)
2. dark red body, gray plastic wheels ($25-40)
3. red body, gray plastic wheels ($50-75)

69B HATRA TRACTOR SHOVEL, issued 1965
1. orange body & shovel, orange wheels with gray plastic tires ($20-30)
2. orange body & shovel, red wheels with black plastic tires ($12-15)
3. orange body & shovel, yellow wheels with black plastic tires ($12-15)
4. yellow body & shovel, red wheels with black plastic tires ($12-15)
5. yellow body & shovel, yellow wheels with black plastic tires ($10-15)

70A FORD THAMES ESTATE CAR, issued 1959
1. yellow & turquoise body, no windows, gray plastic wheels ($25-40)
2. yellow & turquoise body, clear windows, gray plastic wheels ($25-40)
3. yellow & turquoise body, green windows, gray plastic wheels ($25-40)
4. yellow & turquoise body, clear windows, silver plastic wheels ($25-40)
5. yellow & turquoise body, green windows, silver plastic wheels ($25-40)
6. yellow & turquoise body, green windows, black plastic wheels ($20-35)

70B FORD GRIT SPREADER TRUCK, issued 1966
1. red cab, light yellow dump, black plastic pull, black plastic whls. ($5-8)
2. red cab, light yellow dump, gray plastic pull, black plastic wheels ($5-8)
3. red cab, dark yellow dump, gray plastic pull, black plastic whls. ($8-12)
4. red cab, dark yellow dump, black plastic pull, black plastic whls. ($8-12)

71A AUSTIN 200 GALLON WATER TRUCK, issued 1959
1. olive body, black plastic wheels ($25-40)

71B JEEP GLADIATOR PICKUP, issued 1964
1. red body, green interior, black plastic wheels ($35-50)
2. red body, white interior, black plastic wheels ($18-25)

71C FORD HEAVY WRECK TRUCK, issued 1968
1. red cab, white body & chassis, amber windows, red hook, black plastic wheels ($60-75)
2. red cab, white body & chassis, amber windows, yellow hook, black plastic wheels ($60-75)
3. red cab, white body & chassis, green windows, red hook, black plastic wheels ($5-8)
4. red cab, white body & chassis, green windows, yellow hook, black plastic wheels ($5-8)

72A FORDSON TRACTOR, issued 1959
1. blue body, gray plastic front wheels, gray plastic tires with orange wheels ($30-45)
2. blue body, black plastic front wheels, black plastic tires with orange wheels ($30-45)
3. blue body, gray plastic tires with orange wheels front & rear ($25-40)
4. blue body, gray plastic tires with yellow wheels front & rear ($75-100)
5. blue body, black plastic tires with yellow wheels front & rear (75-100)
6. blue body, black plastic tires with orange wheels front & rear ($25-40)

72B STANDARD JEEP, issued 1966
1. yellow body, yellow wheels with black plastic tires ($5-8)

73A 10 TON PRESSURE REFUELLER, issued 1959
1. bluish-gray body, gray plastic wheels ($35-50)

73B FERRARI F1 RACING CAR, issued 1962
1. red body, gray driver ($20-25)
2. red body, white driver ($20-25)

73C MERCURY STATION WAGON, issued 1968
1. metallic lime green body, black plastic tires ($5-8)

74A MOBILE REFRESHMENT CANTEEN, issued 1959
1. white body, blue base & interior, gray plastic wheels ($300-350)
2. pink body, light blue base, gray plastic wheels ($300-500)
3. pinkish cream body, blue base & interior, gray plastic wheels ($300-350)
4. cream body, blue base & interior, gray plastic wheels ($300-350)
5. silver body, blue base & interior, gray plastic wheels ($25-40)
6. silver body, aqua base & interior, gray plastic wheels ($25-40)
7. silver body, blue base & interior, silver plastic wheels ($25-40)
8. silver body, aqua base & interior, silver plastic wheels ($25-40)
9. silver body, pale blue base & interior, gray plastic wheels ($25-40)
10. silver body, dark blue base & interior, gray plastic wheels ($25-40)

74B DAIMLER BUS, issued 1966
1. cream body, "Esso Extra Petrol" decals, black plastic wheels ($10-15)

2. cream body, "Esso Extra Petrol" labels, black plastic wheels ($10-15)
3. green body, "Esso Extra Petrol" labels, black plastic wheels ($8-12)
4. red body, "Esso Extra Petrol" labels, black plastic wheels ($7-10)

75A FORD THUNDERBIRD, issued 1960
1. cream & pink body, black baseplate, gray plastic wheels ($45-60)
2. cream & pink body, black baseplate, silver plastic wheels ($45-60)
3. cream & pink body, dark blue baseplate, silver plastic wheels ($45-60)
4. cream & pink body, bluish green baseplate, silver plastic wheels ($45-60)
5. cream & pink body, black baseplate, black plastic wheels ($75-90)

75B FERRARI BERLINETTA, issued 1965
1. met. light blue body, spoked wheels with black plastic tires, unpainted base ($50-75)
2. light green body, spoked wheels with black plastic tires, unpainted base ($7-10)
3. light green body, spoked wheels with black plastic tires, silver-gray base ($10-15)
4. dark green body, silver wheels with black plastic tires, unpainted base ($7-10)
5. red body, silver wheels with black plastic tires, unpainted base ($450-650)

MODELS OF YESTERYEAR

Y- 1A 1925 Allchin Traction Engine   2 2/3"   1956
Y- 1B 1911 Ford Model T   3"   1964
Y- 2A 1911 "B" Type Bus   2 2/3"   1956
Y- 2B 1911 Renault Two Seater   3"   1963
Y- 3A 1907 London "E" Class Tram Car   3 1/8"   1956
Y- 3B 1910 Benz Limousine   3 1/4"   1966
Y- 4A Sentinel Steam Wagon   2 3/4"   1956
Y- 4B Shand Mason Horse Drawn Fire Engine   3 1/2"   1960
Y- 4C 1909 Opel Coupe   3 1/8"   1966
Y- 5A 1929 LeMans Bentley   3 1/8"   1957
Y- 5B 1929 4 1/2 Litre Bentley   3 1/2"   1962
Y- 5C 1907 Peugeot   3 2/3"   1969
Y- 6A 1916 A.E.C. "Y" Type Lorry   2 3/4"   1957
Y- 6B 1926 Type 35 Bugatti   3 1/8"   1961
Y- 6C 1913 Cadillac   3 3/8"   1967
Y- 7A 1914 Ton Leyland Van   2 3/4"   1957
Y- 7B 1913 Mercer Raceabout   3 1/4"   1961

Y- 7C 1912 Rolls Royce   3 3/4"   1968
Y- 8A 1926 Morris Cowley "Bullnose"   2 1/2"   1958
Y- 8B 1914 Sunbeam Motorcycle & Sidecar   2 2/3"   1962
Y- 8C 1914 Stutz Roadster   3 3/8"   1969
Y- 9A 1924 Fowler Showman's Engine   3 1/4"   1958
Y- 9B 1912 Simplex   3 3/4"   1968
Y-10A 1908 Grand Prix Mercedes   2 7/8"   1958
Y-10B 1928 Mercedes Benz 36/220   3 3/4"   1963
Y-10C 1906 Rolls Royce Silver Ghost   3 2/3"   1969
Y-11A 1920 Aveling & Porter Steam Roller   3 1/8"   1959
Y-11B 1912 Packard Landaulet   3 1/4"   1964
Y-12A 1899 London Horse Drawn Bus   3 1/2"   1959
Y-12B 1909 Thomas Flyabout   4"   1967
Y-13A 1862 Santa Fe Locomotive   3 1/3"   1959
Y-13B 1911 Daimler   3 1/3"   1966
Y-14A 1903 Duke of Connaught Locomotive   3"   1959
Y-14B 1911 Maxwell Roadster   3 1/4"   1965

Y-15A 1907 Rolls Royce Silver Ghost   3 1/4"   1960
Y-15B Packard Victoria   4 1/2"   1969
Y-16A Spyker   3 1/3"   1961

VARIATIONS

Y- 1A 1925 ALLCHIN TRACTION ENGINE, issued 1956
1. green body, straight unpainted treads, copper boiler door ($125-150)
2. green body, diagonal unpainted treads, copper boiler door ($85-100)
3. green body, diagonal red painted treads, copper boiler door ($75-90)
4. green body, diagonal unpainted treads, gold boiler door ($85-100)
5. green body, diagonal red painted treads, gold boiler door ($75-90)
6. green body, smooth unpainted treads, gold boiler door ($450-600)
7. green body, diagonal unpainted treads, silver boiler door ($125-150)

Y- 1B 1911 FORD MODEL T FORD, issued 1964
1. red body & chassis, black roof, black seats, red metal steering wheel ($18-25)
2. red body & chassis, black roof, black seats, black plastic steering wheel ($18-25)
3. silver plated body & chassis, red roof & seats, black plastic steering wheel ($45-60)
4. gold plated body & chassis, red roof & seats, black plastic steering wheel ($45-60)
5. silver plated body & chassis, black roof & seats, black plastic steering wheel ($45-60)

Y- 2A 1911 'B' TYPE LONDON BUS, issued 1956
1. red body, unpainted wheels, black driver, 4 over 4 side windows ($200-250)
2. red body, unpainted wheels, blue driver, 4 over 4 side windows ($200-250)
3. red body, unpainted wheels, black driver, 8 over 4 side windows ($60-75)
4. red body, unpainted wheels, blue driver, 8 over 4 side windows ($60-75)
5. red body, black wheels, black driver, 8 over 4 side windows ($60-75)
6. red body, black wheels, blue driver, 8 over 4 side windows ($60-75)

Y- 2B 1911 RENAULT TWO SEATER, issued 1963
1. green body, unplated dash board & wheels, green metal steering wheel ($30-35)
2. green body, brass dashboard & wheels, green metal steering wheel ($20-25)
3. green body, brass dashboard & wheels, black plastic steering wheel ($20-25)
4. silver plated body, silver plated dashboard, wheels & steering wheel ($45-60)

Y- 3A 1907 LONDON 'E' CLASS TRAMCAR, issued 1956
1. red body, cream roof, gray metal wheels, "Dewars" decals ($450-550)
2. red body, cream roof, gray metal wheels, "News of The World" decals ($60-75)
3. red body, white roof, black plastic wheels, "News of The World" decals ($60-75)
4. red body, white roof, black plastic wheels, "News of The World" decals ($60-75)

Y- 3B 1910 BENZ LIMOUSINE, issued 1966
1. cream body, green roof, seats & grille, metal steering wheel, high cast lights ($40-50)
2. cream body, green roof, red seats & grille, metal steering wheel, high cast headlights ($40-50)
3. cream body, green roof, seats & grille, metal steering wheel, low cast lights ($25-40)
4. cream body, chartreuse roof, green seats & grille, metal steering wheel ($130-150)
5. cream body, chartreuse roof, red seats & grille, metal steering wheel ($130-150)
6. cream body, green roof, red seats & grille, metal steering wheel ($25-40)
7. lt. green body, green roof, seats & grille, metal steering wheel ($60-75)
8. lt. green body, green roof, red seats & grille, metal steering wheel ($60-75)
9. lt. green body, chartreuse roof, red sets & grille, metal steering wheel ($25-40)

10. lt. green body, chartreuse roof, red seats, green grille, metal steering wheel ($25-40)
11. lt. green body, chartreuse roof, red seats, black grille, metal steering wheel ($35-50)
12. lt. chartreuse roof, red seats & grille, plastic steering wheel ($25-40)
13. lt. chartreuse roof, red seats, green grille, plastic steering wheel ($25-40)
14. lt. chartreuse roof, red seats, black grille, plastic steering wheel ($25-40)
15. lt. green body, black roof, red seats & grille, metal steering wheel ($18-25)
16. lt. green body, black roof, red seats & green grille, metal steering wheel ($18-25)
17. lt. green body, black roof, red seats & grille, metal steering wheel ($18-25)
18. lt. green body, black roof, red seats, green grille, plastic steering wheel ($18-25)
19. dk. green body, lime roof, red seats & grille, plastic steering wheel ($45-60)
20. dk. green body, lime roof, red seats & grille, plastic steering wheel ($45-60)
21. dk. green, black roof, red seats & grille, plastic steering wheel ($15-20)
22. dk. green, black roof, red seats, green grille, plastic steering wheel ($18-25)

Y- 4A SENTINEL STEAM WAGON, issued 1956
1. blue body, unpainted metal wheels ($50-65)
2. blue body, black plastic wheels ($175-225)

Y- 4B SHAND MASON HORSE DRAWN FIRE ENGINE, issued 1960
1. red body, gray horses, "Kent" decals, gold boiler ($250-300)
2. red body, white horses, "Kent" decals, gold boiler ($150-175)
3. red body, white horses, blue bordered "London" decals, gold boiler ($150-175)
4. red body, white horses, black bordered "London" decals, gold boiler ($150-175)
5. red body, white horses, black bordered "London" decals, silver boiler
6. red body, black horses, black bordered "London" decals, silver boiler ($150-175)
7. red body, black horses, black bordered "London" decals, gold boiler ($135-150)
8. red body, black horses, gold bordered "London" decals, gold boiler ($135-150)
9. red body, black horses, gold bordered "London" decals, silver boiler ($150-175)

Y- 4B 1909 OPEL COUPE, issued 1967
1. white body, maroon seats & grille, smooth tan roof ($25-30)
2. white body, maroon seats, red grille, smooth tan roof ($25-30)
3. white body, red seats & grille, smooth tan roof ($18-25)
4. white body, red seats & grille, textured tan roof ($35-50)
5. gold plated body, red seats & grille, smooth red roof ($45-60)
6. silver plated body, red seats & grille, smooth red roof ($45-60)

Y- 5A 1929 LEMANS BENTLEY, issued 1958
1. silver radiator & grille, gray tonneau, silver steering wheel ($150-175)
2. silver radiator, green grille, gray tonneau, silver steering whl ($150-175)
3. gold radiator, green grille, gray tonneau, silver steering wheel ($150-175)
4. gold radiator, green grille, green tonneau, silver steering wheel ($60-75)
5. green radiator, green grille, green tonneau, silver steering wheel ($60-75)
6. gold radiator, green grille, green tonneau, green steering wheel ($60-75)

Y- 5B 1929 4 1/2 LITRE BENTLEY, issued 1962
1. met. apple green body & radiator shell, green seats & tonneau, "5" decal ($350-400)
2. met. apple green body & radiator shell, red seats & tonneau, "5" decal ($350-400)
3. met. green body & radiator shell, green seats & tonneau, "5" decal ($350-400)
4. green body & radiator shell, green seats & tonneau, "5" decal ($30-45)
5. green body & radiator shell, red seats & tonneau, "5" decal ($30-45)
6. green body, unpainted radiator shell, red seats & tonneau, "5" decal

($30-45)
7. green body, unpainted radiator shell, red seats & tonneau, "3" decal ($35-50)
8. green body, unpainted radiator shell, red seats & tonneau, "6" decal ($50-60)
9. silver plated body & radiator shell, green seats & tonneau, "5" decal ($50-65)
10. silver plated body & radiator shell, red seats & tonneau, "5" decal ($50-65)

Y-5C 1907 PEUGEOT, issued 1969
1. yellow body & chassis, black roof, red seats & grille, amber windows ($18-25)
2. yellow body & chassis, black roof, red seats & grille, clear windows ($50-75)

Y-6A 1916 AEC "Y" TYPE LORRY, issued 1957
1. light gray body, metal wheels ($75-90)
2. dark gray body, metal wheels ($85-100)
3. dark gray body, black plastic wheels ($1200-1500)

Y-6B 1926 TYPE 35 BUGATTI, issued 1961
1. blue body, red dash & floor, gray plastic tires, "6" decal ($100-125)
2. blue body, red dash & floor, black plastic tires, "6" decal ($25-40)
3. blue body, red dash & floor, black plastic tires, "6" decal, blue grille ($70-80)
4. blue body, red dash & floor, black plastic tires, "9" decal ($35-50)
5. blue body, white dash & floor, black plastic tires, "6" decal ($125-150)
6. red body, white dash & floor, black plastic tires, "6" decal ($25-40)
7. red body, white dash & floor, black plastic tires, "5" decal ($40-55)
8. red body, black dash & floor, black plastic tires, "6" decal ($125-150)
9. red body, white dash & floor, black plastic tires, "9" decal ($40-50)
10. silver plated body, dash & floor, black plastic tires, no decal ($200-250)

Y-6C 1913 CADILLAC, issued 1967
1. yellow-gold body & chassis, maroon roof, grille & seat ($20-25)
2. dark gold body & chassis, maroon roof, grille & seat ($20-25)

3. dark gold body & chassis, maroon roof, grille & seat, "913" base date ($45-60)
4. brown gold body & chassis, maroon roof, grille & seat ($20-25)
5. silver plated body & chassis, maroon roof, grille & seat ($125-150)
6. gold plated body & chassis, maroon roof, grille & seat ($150-175)

Y-7A 1914 TON LEYLAND VAN, issued 1957
1. dark red-brown body, cream roof, metal wheels, without central line decal ($850-1000)
2. dark red-brown body, white roof, metal wheels, full text decal ($75-90)
3. dark red-brown body, cream roof, metal wheels, full text decal ($75-90)
4. light red-brown body, cream roof, metal wheels, full text decal ($75-90)
5. light red-brown body, cream roof, black plastic wheels, full text decal ($1200-1500)

Y-7B 1913 MERCER RACEABOUT, issued 1961
1. lilac body & grille, gray plastic tires ($90-125)
2. lilac body & grille, black plastic tires ($35-50)
3. yellow body & grille, black plastic tires ($20-35)
4. yellow body, gold grille, black plastic tires ($20-35)
5. silver plated body & grille, black plastic tires ($175-200)
6. gold plated body & grille, black plastic tires ($200-250)

Y-7C 1912 ROLLS ROYCE, issued 1968
1. silver body, red base, smooth gray roof, red seats & grille ($20-35)
2. silver body, red base, smooth red roof, red seats & grille ($25-40)
3. silver body, red base, ribbed gray roof, red seats & grille ($175-200)
4. silver body, red base, ribbed red roof, red seats & grille ($25-40)
5. silver plated body & base, gray smooth roof, red seats & grille ($50-60)
6. silver plated body & base, gray ribbed roof, red seats & grille ($50-60)
7. silver plated body & base, red ribbed roof, red seats & grille ($50-60)
8. gold plated body & base, red ribbed roof, red seats & grille ($50-60)

Y-8A 1926 MORRIS COWLEY "BULLNOSE", issued 1958
1. light tan body, brown base, copper wheels ($50-75)
2. light tan body, brown base, unplated wheels ($50-75)
3. dark tan body, brown base, unplated wheels ($50-75)

Y- 8B 1914 SUNBEAM MOTORCYCLE & SIDECAR, issued 1962
1. silver plated body, black sidecar seat ($1200-1500)
2. silver plated body, bright green sidecar seat ($350-500)
3. silver plated body, dark green sidecar seat ($35-50)

Y- 8C 1914 STUTZ ROADSTER, issued 1969
1. met. red body & chassis, smooth tan roof, gold gas tank ($50-75)
2. met. red body & chassis, smooth tan roof, copper gas tank ($18-25)
3. met. red body & chassis, textured tan roof, copper gas tank ($18-25)

Y- 9-A FOWLER SHOWMAN'S ENGINE, issued 1958
1. dk. maroon body, cream roof, copper boiler, gold roof supports, cream roof spreaders, black base insert ($90-110)
2. dk. maroon body, cream roof, copper boiler, gold roof supports, cream roof spreaders dark maroon base insert ($75-90)
3. lt. maroon body, cream roof, gold boiler, gold roof supports, cream roof spreaders, light maroon base insert ($75-90)
4. lt. maroon body, cream roof, gold boiler, white roof supports & roof spreaders ($75-90)
5. lt. maroon body, cream roof, gold boiler, gold roof supports & spreaders ($75-90)
6. lt. maroon body, white roof, gold boiler, gold roof supports & spreaders ($75-90)
7. lt. maroon body, cream roof, silver boiler, silver roof supports & spreaders ($75-90)
8. lt. maroon body, white roof, copper boiler, gold roof supports, cream spreaders black base insert ($90-110)
9. red body, cream roof, gold boiler, gold roof supports & spreaders ($75-90)
10. red body, white roof, gold boiler, gold roof supports & spreaders ($75-90)
11. red body, cream roof, gold boiler, cream roof supports & spreaders ($75-90)
12. red body, white roof, gold boiler, silver roof supports & spreaders ($75-90)
13. red body, white roof, silver boiler, silver roof supports & spreaders ($75-90)

14. red body, white roof, silver boiler, gold roof supports & spreaders ($75-90)
15. red body, white roof, gold boiler, gold roof supports & spreaders, black base insert ($90-110)

Y- 9B 1912 SIMPLEX, issued 1968
1. yellow-green body & chassis, smooth tan roof, red seats ($25-35)
2. dark green body & chassis, smooth tan roof, red seats ($25-35)
3. dark green body & chassis, textured tan roof, red seats ($40-50)
4. bronze-gold body, red-brown chassis, textured black roof, red seats ($45-60)
5. bronze-gold body, red-brown chassis, textured black roof, dark red seats ($45-60)

Y-10A 1908 GRAND PRIX MERCEDES, issued 1958
1. white body, light green seats, silver trim ($125-150)
2. cream body, light green seats, silver trim ($65-80)
3. cream body, light green seats, gold trim ($65-80)
4. cream body, dark green seats, gold trim ($65-80)
5. cream body, dark green seats, silver trim ($65-80)
6. cream body, dark green seats, no trim ($65-80)

Y-10B 1928 MERCEDES-BENZ 36/220, issued 1963
1. white body, beige dashboard, double spare tires ($45-60)
2. white body, beige dashboard, single spare tire ($18-25)
3. gold plated body & dashboard, single spare tire ($45-60)
4. silver plated body & dashboard, single spare tire ($45-60)
5. silver plated body & dashboard, double spare tires ($45-60)

Y-10C 1906 ROLLS ROYCE SILVER GHOST, issued 1969
1. lime body, gray-brown chassis, maroon seats & grille ($18-25)
2. lime body, gray-brown chassis, brown-red seats, maroon grille ($18-25)

Y-11A 1920 AVELING PORTER STEAM ROLLER, issued 1958
1. green body, black roof supports, dark brown flywheel ($65-80)
2. green body, black roof supports, matt black flywheel ($65-80)
3. green body, black roof supports, gloss black flywheel ($65-80)

4. green body, green roof supports, dark brown flywheel ($65-80)
5. green body, green roof supports, matt black flywheel ($65-80)
6. green body, green roof supports, gloss black flywheel ($65-80)

Y-11B 1912 PACKARD LAUNDAULET, issued 1964
1. red body, metal steering wheel, unplated grille & wheels ($20-35)
2. red body, metal steering wheel, brass grille & wheels ($20-35)
3. red body, plastic steering wheel, unplated grille & wheels ($20-35)
4. red body, plastic steering wheel, brass grille & wheels ($20-35)
5. dark red body, plastic steering wheel, brass grille & wheels ($20-35)

Y-12A 1899 LONDON HORSE DRAWN BUS, issued 1959
1. red body, beige driver & seats, light brown horses ($65-80)
2. red body, beige driver & seats, dark brown horses ($65-80)
3. red body, pink-cream driver & seats, dark brown horses ($75-90)

Y-12B 1909 THOMAS FLYABOUT issued 1967
1. blue body & chassis, smooth tan roof, yellow seats & grille ($850-1000)
2. blue body & chassis, smooth tan roof, dark red seats & grille ($18-25)
3. blue body & chassis, textured tan roof, dark red seats & grille ($18-25)
4. silver plated body & chassis, textured tan roof, dark red seats & grille ($45-60)
5. gold plated body & chassis, textured tan roof, dark red seats & grille ($45-60)

Y-13A 1868 SANTA FE LOCOMOTIVE, issued 1959
1. light green body, maroon engine ($250-350)
2. dark green body, maroon engine ($65-80)

Y-13B DAIMLER, issued 1966
1. yellow body, black chassis, black seats & grille ($25-40)
2. yellow body, black chassis, maroon seats, black grille ($25-40)
3. yellow body, black chassis, maroon seats & grille ($25-40)
4. silver plated body & chassis, maroon seats, black grille ($45-60)
5. gold plated body & chassis, maroon seats, black grille ($45-60)
6. dark gold plated body & chassis, maroon seats, black grille ($45-60)

Y-14A 1903 DUKE OF CONNAUGHT LOCOMOTIVE, issued 1959
1. green body, brown frame, gold boiler door ($65-80)
2. green body, brown frame, silver boiler door ($65-80)

Y-14B 1911 MAXWELL ROADSTER, issued 1965
1. turquoise body, black roof, maroon seats, black grille, gold gas tank ($35-50)
2. turquoise body, black roof, maroon seats, black grille, copper gas tank ($18-25)
3. turquoise body, black roof, maroon seats, red grille, copper gas tank ($18-25)
4. silver plated body, red roof, red seats, red grille, plated gas tank ($45-60)
5. gold plated body, red roof, red seats, red grille, plated gas tank ($45-60)

Y-15A 1907 ROLLS ROYCE SILVER GHOST, issued 1960
1. silver-green body, black seats, gray plastic tires, unplated whls ($45-60)
2. silver-green body, black seats, gray plastic tires, brass wheels ($45-60)
3. silver-green body, black seats, black plastic tires, brass wheels ($18-25)
4. silver-green body, black seats, black plastic tires, unplated whls ($18-25)
5. gold plated body, black seats, black plastic tires, plated wheels ($45-60)
6. gold plated body, green seats, black plastic tires, plated wheels ($45-60)
7. silver plated body, black seats, black plastic tires, plated wheels ($45-60)
8. silver plated body, green seats, black plastic tires, plated wheels ($45-60)

Y-15B PACKARD VICTORIA, issued 1969
1. tan body, brown chassis, maroon roof, grille, seats & trunk ($18-25)
2. tan body, brown chassis, maroon roof, red grille maroon seats & trunk ($18-25)

Y-16A 1904 SPYKER, issued 1961
1. light green body, dark green fenders, black plastic tires ($1500-2000)
2. maroon body & fenders, black plastic tires ($900-1200)
3. light yellow body & fenders, gray plastic tires ($90-110)
4. light yellow body & fenders, black plastic tires ($25-40)
5. dark yellow body & fenders, black plastic tires ($20-30)
6. silver plated body & fenders, black plastic tires ($45-60)

MAJOR PACKS

M- 1A Caterpillar Earth Scraper   4 1/2"   1957
M- 1B BP Autotanker   4"   1961
M- 2A Bedford Ice Cream Truck   4 1/3"   1957
M- 2B Bedford Truck & York Trailer   4 5/8"   1961
M- 3A Thornycraft Antar & Centurion Tank   4 1/2"   1959
M- 4A Ruston Bucyrus Power Shovel   3 7/8"   1959
M- 4B GMC Tractor & Freuhof Hopper Train   11 1/4   1964
M- 5A Massey Ferguson Combine Harvester   4 5/8"   1960
M- 6A Pickfords 200 Ton Transporter   11"   1960
M- 6B Racing Car Transporter   5 1/8"   1965
M- 7A Jennings Cattle Truck   4 3/4"   1960
M- 8A Mobilgas Petrol Tanker   3 7/8"   1960
M- 8B Guy Warrior Car Transporter   8 1/4"   1964
M- 9A Interstate Double Freighter   11 1/8"   1962
M-10A Dinkum Dumper   4 1/4"   1962

VARIATIONS

M- 1A CATERPILLAR EARTH SCRAPER, issued 1957
  1. yellow body, silver metal wheels, black plastic tires ($45-60)

M- 1B BP AUTOTANKER, issued 1961
  1. yellow and green body, "BP" decals, black plastic wheels ($15-25)

M- 2A BEDFORD ICE CREAM TRUCK, issued 1957
  1. light blue cab, cream trailer, metal wheels ($45-60)
  2. light blue cab, cream trailer, gray plastic wheels ($45-60)

M- 2B BEDFORD TRACTOR & YORK TRAILER, issued 1961
  1. orange cab, silver trailer, orange base & rear doors, "Davies Tyres" decals, gray plastic wheels ($50-75)
  2. orange cab, silver trailer, orange base & rear doors, "Davies Tyres" decals, black plastic wheels ($50-75)
  3. silver cab, maroon trailer, orange base & rear doors, "LEP" decals, black plastic wheels ($125-150)
  4. silver cab, maroon trailer, black base & orange rear doors, "LEP" decals, black plastic wheels ($45-60)
  5. silver cab, maroon trailer, black base & rear doors, "LEP" decals, black plastic wheels ($45-60)

M- 3A THORNYCRAFT ANTAR & CENTURION TANK, issued 1959
  1. olive green, black plastic wheels, metal wheels on tank ($45-60)

2. olive green, black plastic wheels, black plastic rollers on tank ($45-60)

M- 4A RUSTON BUCYRUS POWER SHOVEL, issued 1959
1. maroon body, yellow shovel assembly, green treads, red lettered decals ($45-60)
2. maroon body, yellow shovel assembly, green treads, yellow lettered decals ($45-60)
3. maroon body, yellow shovel assembly, gray treads, yellow lettered decals ($45-60)

M- 4B GMC TRACTOR & FREUHOF HOPPER TRAIN, issued 1964
1. dark red cab, silver hopper, red plastic wheels with gray plastic tires ($45-60)
2. dark red cab, silver hopper, red plastic wheels with black plastic tires ($45-60)

M- 5A MASSEY FERGUSON COMBINE HARVESTER, issued 1960
1. red body, silver metal front wheels, black plastic rear wheels ($35-50)
2. red body, orange plastic front wheels, black plastic rear wheels ($35-50)
3. red body, yellow plastic front wheels, black plastic rear wheels ($35-50)
4. red body, orange plastic front & rear wheels ($35-50)
5. red body, yellow plastic front & rear wheels ($35-50)

M- 6A PICKFORDS 200 TON TRANSPORTER, issued 1960
1. blue cab, maroon trailer, black plastic wheels ($35-50)
2. blue cab, dark red trailer, black plastic wheels ($35-50)

M- 6B RACING CAR TRANSPORTER, issued 1965
1. green body, black plastic tires ($25-40)

M- 7A JENNINGS CATTLE TRUCK, issued 1960
1. red cab, tan trailer, gray plastic wheels ($45-60)
2. red cab, tan trailer, black plastic wheels ($40-55)
3. red cab, dark tan trailer, black plastic wheels ($40-55)

M- 8A MOBILGAS PETROL TANKER, issued 1960
1. red cab & trailer, gray plastic wheels ($75-90)
2. red cab & trailer, black plastic wheels ($75-90)

M- 8B GUY WARRIOR CAR TRANSPORTER, issued 1964
1. blue-green cab, orange trailer, orange wheels, gray plastic tires ($25-40)

M- 9A INTERSTATE DOUBLE FREIGHTER, issued 1962
1. blue cab, gray trailers, unpainted connector, yellow background decals ($60-75)
2. blue cab, gray trailers, blue connector, yellow background decals ($60-75)
3. blue cab, silver trailers, unpainted connector, yellow background decals ($60-75)
4. blue cab, silver trailers, blue connector, yellow background decals ($60-75)
5. blue cab, silver trailers, unpainted connector, orange background decals ($60-75)

M-10A DINKUM DUMPER, issued 1962
1. yellow body and dumper, silver metal wheels, black plastic tires ($30-45)
2. yellow body and dumper, red plastic wheels, black plastic tires ($30-45)

KING-SIZE

K- 1A Weatherhill Hydraulic Shovel   3 7/10"   1960
K- 1B Hoveringham Tipper Truck   4 1/4"   1964
K- 2A Muir Hill Dumper   3"   1960
K- 2B K.W. Dump Truck   5 2/3"   1964
K- 2C Scammell Heavy Wreck Truck   4 3/4"   1969
K- 3A Caterpillar Bulldozer   3 1/3"   1960
K- 3B Hatra Tractor Shovel   5-9/10   1965
K- 4A International Tractor   2-4/5"   1960
K- 4B GMC Tractor & Freuhof Hopper Train   11 1/4"   1967
K- 4C Leyland Tipper   4 1/2"   1969
K- 5A Foden Tipper Truck   4 1/4"   1961
K- 5B Racing Car Transporter   5 1/8"   1967
K- 6A Allis-Chalmers Earth Scraper   5 7/8"   1961
K- 6B Mercedes Benz "Binz" Ambulance   4 1/8"   1967
K- 7A Curtiss Wright Rear Dumper   5 3/4"   1961
K- 7B Refuse Truck   4 3/5"   1967
K- 8A Prime Mover & Caterpillar Tractor   12 1/2"   1962
K- 8B Guy Warrior Car Transporter   8 1/4"   1967
K- 9A Diesel Road Roller   3 3/4"   1962

K- 9B Claas Combine Harvester   5 1/2"   1967
K-10A Aveling Barford Tractor Shovel   4 1/8"   1963
K-10B Pipe Truck   8"   1967
K-11A Fordson Tractor & Farm Trailer   6 1/4"   1963
K-11B DAF Car Transporter   9"   1969
K-12A Heavy Breakdown Wreck Truck   4 3/4"   1963
K-12B Scammell Crane Truck   6"   1969
K-13A Readymix Concrete Truck   5 1/8"   1963
K-14A Taylor Jumbo Crane   5"   1964
K-15A Merryweather Fire Engine   6"   1964
K-16A Dodge Tractor with Twin Tipper   11 7/8"   1966
K-17A Low Loader with Bulldozer   9 1/2"   1967
K-18A Articulated Horse Box   6 1/2"   1967
K-19A Scammell Tipper Truck   4 3/4"   1967
K-20A Tractor Transporter   9"   1968
K-21A Mercury Cougar   4 1/8"   1968
K-22A Dodge Charger   4 1/2"   1969
K-23A Mercury Police Commuter   4 3/8"   1969
K-24A Lamborghini Miura   4"   1969

VARIATIONS

K- 1A WEATHERHILL HYDRAULIC SHOVEL, issued 1960
1. yellow body & shovel, black wheels with gray plastic tires ($50-75)

K- 1B HOVERINGHAM TIPPER TRUCK, issued 1964
1. red cab & chassis, orange dumper, "Hoveringham" decals, black plastic tires ($20-35)

K- 2A MUIR HILL DUMPER, issued 1960
1. red body and dump, green metal wheels, gray plastic tires ($25-40)
2. red body and dump, green metal wheels, black plastic tires ($20-35)

K- 2B K.W. DUMP TRUCK, issued 1964
1. yellow body and dump, red plastic whls with black plastic tires ($20-35)

K- 2C SCAMMELL HEAVY WRECK TRUCK, issued 1969
1. white body, green windows, black plastic tires ($25-35)
2. white body, amber windows, black plastic tires ($15-20)
3. gold body, amber windows, black plastic tires ($25-40)

K- 3A CATERPILLAR BULLDOZER, issued 1960
1. yellow body, gray metal rollers ($25-40)
2. yellow body, red plastic rollers ($25-40)
3. yellow body, yellow plastic rollers ($25-40)

K- 3B HATRA TRACTOR SHOVEL, issued 1965
1. orange body & shovel, red plastic wheels, black plastic tires ($20-30)

K- 4A INTERNATIONAL TRACTOR, issued 1960
1. red body, green metal wheels, black plastic tires ($25-40)
2. red body, red metal wheels, black plastic tires ($25-40)
3. red body, red plastic wheels, black plastic tires ($20-35)
4. red body, orange plastic wheels, black plastic tires ($20-35)

K- 4B G.M.C. TRACTOR & FREUHOF HOPPER TRAIN, issued 1967
1. dark red cab, silver hoppers, red plastic wheels with gray plastic tires ($35-50)
2. dark red cab, silver hoppers, red plastic wheels with black plastic tires ($25-40)

K- 4C LEYLAND TIPPER, issued 1969
1. dark red cab, silver dump, "LE Transport" labels, black plastic tires ($15-20)
2. dark red cab, silver dump, "W. Wates" labels, black plastic tires ($18-25)
3. pea green cab & dump, "W. Wates" labels, black plastic tires ($50-75)
4. orange-red cab, pea green dump, "W. Wates" labels, black plastic tires ($18-25)

K- 5A FODEN TIPPER TRUCK, issued 1961
1. yellow cab and dump, silver metal wheels, black plastic tires ($25-40)
2. yellow cab and dump, red plastic wheels, black plastic tires ($20-35)

K- 5B RACING CAR TRANSPORTER, issued 1967
1. green body, black plastic wheels ($20-35)

K- 6A ALLIS-CHALMERS EARTH SCRAPER, issued 1961
1. orange body, silver metal wheels, black plastic tires ($25-40)
2. orange body, red plastic wheels, black plastic tires ($25-40)

K- 6B MERCEDES BENZ "BINZ" AMBULANCE, issued 1967
1. cream body, silver wheels with black plastic tires ($12-18)

K- 7A CURTIS WRIGHT REAR DUMPER, issued 1961
1. yellow body, silver metal wheels, black plastic tires ($25-40)

K- 7B REFUSE TRUCK, issued 1967
1. red cab, all silver rear tipper, black plastic tires ($12-18)

K- 8A PRIME MOVER & CATERPILLAR TRACTOR, issued 1962
1. orange mover with silver metal wheels; tractor with metal rollers ($50-75)
2. orange mover with silver metal wheels; tractor with orange plastic rollers ($50-75)

3. orange mover with red plastic wheels; tractor with metal rollers ($50-75)
4. orange mover with red plastic wheels; tractor with red plastic rollers ($50-75)
5. orange mover with red plastic wheels; tractor with orange plastic rollers ($50-75)
6. orange mover with red plastic wheels; tractor with yellow plastic rollers ($50-75)

K- 8B GUY WARRIOR CAR TRANSPORTER, issued 1967
1. blue-green cab, orange trailer, orange wheels, gray plastic tires ($25-40)
2. blue-green cab, orange trailer, orange wheels, black plastic tires ($20-30)
3. blue-green cab, orange trailer, red wheels, black plastic tires ($20-30)
4. blue-green cab, yellow trailer, red wheels, black plastic tires ($35-50)
5. yellow cab, yellow trailer, red wheels, black plastic tires ($18-25)

K- 9A DIESEL ROAD ROLLER, issued 1962
1. green body, gray driver ($25-40)
2. green body, red driver ($20-35)

K- 9B CLAAS COMBINE HARVESTER, issued 1967
1. green body, red blade, green & white "Claas" label, no driver ($18-25)
2. green body, red blade, green & white "Claas" label, white driver ($18-25)
3. red body, yellow blade, green & white "Claas" label, tan driver ($18-25)
4. red body, yellow blade, red & white "Claas" label, tan driver ($18-25)
5. red body, yellow blade, red & white "Claas" label, no driver ($18-25)

K-10A AVELING-BARFORD TRACTOR SHOVEL, issued 1963
1. blue-green body, silver metal wheels, black plastic tires, air cleaner cast ($25-40)
2. blue-green body, red plastic wheels, black plastic tires, air cleaner cast ($25-40)
3. blue-green body, red plastic wheels, black plastic tires, no air cleaner cast ($25-40)
4. mint green body, red plastic wheels, black plastic tires, no air cleaner cast ($25-40)

K-10B PIPE TRUCK, issued 1967
1. yellow body and trailer, gray plastic pipes, black plastic tires ($18-25)

K-11A FORDSON TRACTOR & FARM TRAILER, issued 1963
1. blue tractor, silver steering wheel, orange metal wheels ($25-40)
2. blue tractor, silver steering wheel, orange plastic wheels ($20-30)
3. blue tractor, blue steering wheel, orange plastic wheels ($20-30)
4. blue tractor, blue steering wheel, red plastic wheels ($20-30)

K-11B DAF CAR TRANSPORTER, issued 1969
1. met. blue cab, gold trailer, black wheel blocks, black plastic tires ($35-50)
2. yellow cab, orange trailer, black wheel blocks, black plastic tires ($18-25)
3. yellow cab, orange trailer, red wheel blocks, black plastic tires ($18-25)

K-12A HEAVY BREAKDOWN WRECK TRUCK, issued 1963
1. green body, silver metal wheels, no roof lights cast ($25-40)
2. green body, red plastic wheels, no roof lights cast ($25-40)
3. green body, red plastic wheels, with roof lights cast ($25-40)

K-12B SCAMMELL CRANE TRUCK, issued 1969
1. yellow body and crane, red plastic wheels, black plastic tires ($15-20)

K-13A READYMIX CONCRETE TRUCK, issued 1963
1. orange body, silver metal wheels, "Readymix" decals ($25-40)
2. orange body, red plastic wheels, "Readymix" decals ($25-40)
3. orange body, red plastic wheels, "RMC" decals ($25-40)

K-14A TAYLOR JUMBO CRANE, issued 1964
1. yellow body and crane, yellow weight box, red plastic wheels ($18-25)
2. yellow body and crane, red weight box, red plastic wheels ($18-25)

K-15A MERRYWEATHER FIRE ENGINE, issued 1964
1. red body, gray ladder, red plastic wheels, black plastic tires ($18-25)

K-16A DODGE TRACTOR WITH TWIN TIPPERS, issued 1966
1. green cab, yellow tippers, red plastic wheels, black plastic tires ($35-50)

K-17A LOWLOADER WITH BULLDOZER, issued 1967
1. green cab and trailer, "Laing" decals, red & dark yellow bulldozer ($25-40)
2. green cab and trailer, "Taylor Woodrow" decals, red & dark yellow bulldozer ($25-40)

K-18A ARTICULATED HORSE BOX, issued 1967
1. red cab, tan box, black plastic tires, gray rear trailer interior ($18-25)
2. red cab, tan box, black plastic tires, green rear trailer interior ($25-40)
3. red cab, tan box, black plastic tires, red rear trailer interior ($25-40)
4. red cab, tan box, black plastic tires, brown rear trailer interior ($25-40)
5. red cab, tan box, black plastic wheels, multi-colored trailer interior ($25-40)

K-19A SCAMMELL TIPPER TRUCK, issued 1967
1. red cab, yellow tipper, black plastic tires ($15-20)
2. red cab, orange-yellow tipper, black plastic tires ($15-20)

K-20A TRACTOR TRANSPORTER, issued 1968
1. red cab with yellow tanks, red trailer, blue tractors, black plastic tires ($35-50)
2. red cab with red tanks, red trailer, blue tractors, black plastic tires ($35-50)

K-21A MERCURY COUGAR, issued 1968
1. gold body, white interior, black plastic tires ($25-40)
2. gold body, red interior, black plastic tires ($12-18)

K-22A DODGE CHARGER, issued 1969
1. dark blue body, pale blue interior, black plastic tires ($12-18)

K-23A MERCURY POLICE COMMUTER, issued 1969
1. white body, black plastic tires ($12-18)

K-24A LAMBORGHINI MIURA, issued 1969
1. red body, red trunk, silver plastic wheels with black plastic tires ($12-18)
2. red body, red trunk, silver plastic mag wheels with black plastic tires ($12-18)

ACCESSORY PACKS

A- 1A Esso Petrol Pumps and Sign   4 1/2"   1957
A- 1B BP Petrol Pumps and Sign   4 1/2"   1963
A- 2A Bedford Car Transporter   6 1/2"   1957
A- 3A Garage   3"   1957
A- 4A Road Signs   -   1960
A- 5A Home Store   3"   1961
MF-1A Matchbox Fire Station   9 3/4"   1963
MG-1A Matchbox One Story Garage   -   1959
MG-1B Matchbox Two Story Garage   9 1/4"   1961
MG-1C Matchbox Service Station   -   1968

VARIATIONS

A- 1A ESSO PETROL PUMPS AND SIGN, issued 1957
1. red metal pumps and sign ($30-45)

A- 1B BP PETROL PUMPS AND SIGN, issued 1963
1. white metal pumps and sign ($12-15)

A- 2A BEDFORD CAR TRANSPORTER, issued 1957

1. blue cab & trailer, black lettered decals, metal wheels ($50-65)
2. blue cab & trailer, orange lettered decals, gray plastic wheels ($50-65)
3. blue cab & trailer, orange lettered decals, black plastic wheels ($50-65)
4. red cab, gray trailer, orange lettered decals, black plastic wheels ($125-150)

A- 3A GARAGE, issued 1957
1. yellow building, maroon roof, green doors ($25-40)

A- 4A ROAD SIGNS, issued 1960
1. eight black metal road signs with different decals ($20-35)

A- 5A HOME STORE, issued 1961
1. cream building with light green roof ($35-50)

MF- 1A MATCHBOX FIRE STATION, issued 1963
1. cream building with green roof ($125-150)
2. white building with red roof ($35-50)

MG- 1A MATCHBOX ONE STORY GARAGE, issued 1959
1. one story building- yellow building, red base and clock ($95-120)
2. one story building- red building, yellow base and clock ($95-120)

MG- 1B MATCHBOX TWO STORY GARAGE, issued 1961
1. two story building- yellow building, red base, "Esso" decals ($95-120)
2. two story building- white building, green base, "BP" decals ($45-60)

MG- 1C MATCHBOX SERVICE STATION, issued 1968
1. one story white building w/ separate plastic pumps, "BP" livery ($20-35)

ROADWAY SERIES

R- 1A Roadway Layout   1960
R- 1B Roadway   1962
R- 1C Roadway   1964 ($20 -35)
R- 1D Roadway   1968 ($12-15)
R- 2A Roadway Layout- "Heart of London"   1961
R- 2B Construction Set   1968
R- 2C Construction Set   1969 ($12-15)
R- 3A Roadway Layout- "Royal London"   1961
R- 3B Farmyard   1968
R- 4A Racetrack Speedway   1961
R- 4B Grand Prix Race Track   1964

VARIATIONS

R- 1A ROADWAY LAYOUT, issued 1960
1. Lesney Moko and full color picture on outer wrapper ($35-50)

R- 1B ROADWAY, issued 1962
1. Lesney and black and white picture on outer wrapper ($35-50)
2. full color photo with pasture on outer wrapper ($18-25)
3. full color photo with R-1 in blue rectangle in corner on outer wrapper ($8-12)

R- 2A LAYOUT (HEART OF LONDON), issued 1961
1. Big Ben, Tower Bridge & Angel depicted on outer wrapper ($60-75)

R- 2B CONSTRUCTION ROADWAY, issued 1968
1. full color photo depicted constructed buildings on outer wrapper ($12-15)
2. full color photo depicting site off water's edge on outer wrapper ($8-12)

R- 3A ROADWAY LAYOUT (ROYAL LONDON), issued 1961
1. Royal London sites shown on outer wrapper ($60-75)

R- 3B FARM ROADWAY, issued 1968
1. full color farm scene shown on outer wrapper ($8-12)

R- 4A RACETRACK SPEEDWAY, issued 1961
1. black and white racetrack shown on outer sleeve ($25-40)

R- 4B GRAND PRIX RACE TRACK, issued 1964
1. full color scene of four large race cars on outer sleeve ($20-35)

PRESENTATION SETS

The first gift sets were known as "Presentation Sets" and were issued in the United States from only 1957 through 1959. These original sets were not based on any "theme" as gift sets were later. Each of the eight presentation sets contained eight models each and each set contained numerically ordered models. Therefore the PS-1 set consisted of models numbered 1-8, PS-2 had numbers 9-16 and so forth through to PS-8 which contained numbers 57 through 64. The sets contained mostly first issue regular wheels, but by 1957 some of these were already being discontinued for a larger version of the same model and these were included in the presentation sets. The following is a list of the sets:

PS- 1A Presentation Set   1957
PS- 1B Private Owner Set   1959
PS- 2A Presentation Set   1957
PS- 2B Transporter with 4 Cars Set   1959
PS- 3A Presentation Set   1957
PS- 3B Transporter with 6 Cars Set   1959
PS- 4A Presentation set   1958
PS- 4B Commercial Vehicle Set   1959
PS- 5A Presentation Set   1958
PS- 5B Army Transport Set   1959
PS- 6A Presentation Set   1958
PS- 7A Presentation Set   1959
PS- 8A Presentation Set   1959

VARIATIONS

PS-1A PRESENTATION SET, issued 1957
contains 1B, 2A, 3A, 4B, 5B, 6A, 7A, 8A

PS-2A PRESENTATION SET, issued 1957
contains 9A, 10B, 11A, 12A, 13A, 14A, 15A, 16A

PS-3A PRESENTATION SET, issued 1957
contains 17A, 18A, 19A, 20A, 21A, 22A, 23A, 24A

PS-4A PRESENTATION SET, issued 1958
contains 25A, 26A, 27A, 28A, 29A, 30A, 31A, 32A

PS-5A PRESENTATION SET, issued 1958
contains 33A, 34A, 35A, 36A, 37A, 38A, 39A, 40A

PS-6A PRESENTATION SET, issued 1958
contains 41A, 42A, 43A, 44A, 45A, 46A, 47A, 48A

PS-7A PRESENTATION SET, issued 1959
contains 49A, 50A, 51A, 52A, 53A, 54A, 55A, 56A

PS-8A PRESENTATION SET, issued 1959
    contains 57A, 58A, 59A, 60A, 61A, 62A, 63A, 64A

    Later sets issued for England in 1959 started "theme" collecting--army and commercial themes, among others--and were still termed Presentation sets. These sets had lids that lifted to reveal the contents. These include:

PS-1B PRIVATE OWNER SET, issued 1959
    contains 19B, 43A, 45A, A-3A

PS-2B TRANSPORTER & 4 CARS SET, issued 1959
    contains 30A, 31A, 33A, 36A, A-2A

PS-3B TRANSPORTER & 6 CARS SET, issued 1959
    contains 22B, 32A, 33A, 43A, 44A, 45A, A-2A

PS-4B COMMERCIAL VEHICLE SET, issued 1959
    contains 5B, 11B, 21B, 25A, 35A, 40A, 47A, 60A

PS-5A ARMY TRANSPORT SET, issued 1959
    contains 49A, 54A, 55A, 61A, 62A, 63A, M-3A

GIFT SETS

    It was in 1960 that the name "Gift Set" was first used and continued with themes as a basis for each set. Some sets with the same theme and same number may be issued under a different titled set, but are listed below under the same category for simplicity's sake. For valuation combine prices of the individual pieces, then add 10-20% if in a gift box. Sets issued from 1960 through 1969 are listed below:

G- 1A Commercial Motor Set   1960
G- 1B Motorway Set   1964
G- 1C Service Station Set   1966
G- 2A Car Transporter Set   1960
G- 3A Building Constructors Set   1960
G- 3B Farm & Agricultural Set   1963
G- 3C Vacation Set   1966
G- 3D Farm Set   1968
G- 4A Farm Set   1960
G- 4B Grand Prix Racetrack Set   1964
G- 5A Army Set   1960

G- 5B Fire Station Set   1966
G- 5C Famous Cars of Yesteryear   1968
G- 6A Models of Yesteryear Gift Set   1961
G- 6B Commercial Truck Set   1964
G- 7A Models of Yesteryear Gift Set   1960
G- 8A Construction Set   1962
G- 9A Major Pack Set   1962
G- 9B Service Station Set   1964
G-10A Garage Gift Set   1962
G-10B Fire Station Set   1964

VARIATIONS

G- 1A COMMERCIAL VEHICLE SET, issued 1960
    1. contains 5B, 20B, 37B, 47A, 51A, 59A, 60A, 69A (1960)
    2. contains 5C, 10C, 20B, 37B, 46B, 47A, 51A, 69A (1961)
    3. contains 5C, 10C, 12B, 13C, 14C, 21C, 46B, 74A (1962)

G- 1B MOTORWAY SET, issued 1964
  1. contains 6C, 10C, 13C, 33B, 34B, 38B, 48B, 55B, 71B, R-1B

G- 1C SERVICE STATION SET, issued 1966
  1. contains 13D, 31C, 64B, A-1B, MG-1B (1966)
  2. contains 13D, 32C, 56B, MG-1C (1968)

G- 2A CAR TRANSPORTER SET, issued 1960
  1. contains 39A, 44A, 45A, 53A, 66A, 75A, A-2A (1960)
  2. contains 22B, 25B, 33A, 39A, 57B, 75A, A-2A (1961)
  3. contains 25B, 30B, 31B, 39B, 48B, 65B, A-2A (1962)
  4. contains 28C, 32C, 36C, 53B, M-8B (1964)
  5. contains 22C, 28C, 36C, 75B, M-8B or K-8B (1966)
  6. contains 14D, 24C, 31C, 53C, K-8B (1968)

G- 3A BUILDING CONSTRUCTORS SET, issued 1960
  1. contains 2B, 6B, 15B, 16B, 18C, 24B, 28B, M-1A (1960)

G- 3B FARM & AGRICULTURAL SET, issued 1964
  1. contains M-5A, M-7A, K-8A dozer only, K-11A

G- 3C VACATION SET, issued 1966
  1. contains 12C, 23D, 27D, 42B, 45B, 48B, 56B, 68B

G- 3D FARM SET, issued 1968
  1. contains 4D, 12C, 37C, 39C, 40C, 43C, 65C, 72B

G- 4A FARM SET, issued 1960
  1. contains 12B, 23B, 31B, 35A, 72A, M-7A (1960)
  2. contains 12B, 23B, 31B, 35A, 50A, 72A, M-7A (1961)

G- 4B GRAND PRIX RACETRACK SET, issued 1963
  1. contains 13C, 14C, 19C, 32B, 41B, 47B, 57A, 73B, M-1B, R-4B (1963)
  2. contains 13D, 19D orange & green, 29C, 41C white & yellow, 52D red
     & blue, 54B, K-5B or M-6B, R-4B (1966) "Racetrack set"
  3. contains 3C, 8E, 19D green & orange, 25D, 29C, 41C, 52A red & blue,
     67B "Race N Rallye" (1968)

G- 5A ARMY SET, issued 1960
  1. contains 54A, 62A, 63A, 64A, 67A, 68A, M-3A (1960)
  2. contains 12B, 49A, 54A, 61A, 64A, 67A, M-3A (1964)

G- 5B FIRE STATION SET, issued 1966
  1. contains 29C, 54B, 59C, MF-1A

G- 5C FAMOUS CARS OF YESTERYEAR, issued 1968
  1. contains Y-4B, Y-9B, Y-12B, Y-14B

G- 6A MODELS OF YESTERYEAR GIFT SET, issued 1961
  1. contains Y-1A, Y-2A, Y-5A, Y-10A, Y-13A (1961)
  2. contains Y-6A, Y-7A, Y-10A, Y-15A, Y-16A (1962)
  3. contains Y-5B, Y-6A, Y-7B, Y-15A, Y-16A (1963)

G- 6B COMMERCIAL TRUCK SET, issued 1964
  1. contains 6C, 15C, 16C, 17D, 26B, 30B, 58B, 62B (1964)
  2. contains 16C, 17D, 25C, 26B, 30C, 69B, 70B, 71B (1966)
  3. contains 1E, 10D, 21D, 26C, 30C, 49B, 60B, 70B (1968)

G- 7A MODELS OF YESTERYEAR GIFT SET, issued 1961
  1. contains Y-3A, Y-8A, Y-9A, Y-12A, Y-14A (1961)
  2. contains Y-3A, Y-4B, Y-11A, Y-12A, Y-13A (1962)
  3. contains Y-2B, Y-5B, Y-10B, Y-15B, Y-16B (1964)
  4. contains, Y-1B, Y-3B, Y-11B, Y-14B (1966)

G- 8A CONSTRUCTION SET, issued 1962
  1. contains K-1A, K-2A, K-3A, K-5A, K-6A (1962)
  2. contains K-1B, K-7A, K-10A, K-13A, K-14A (1964)
  3. contains K-1B, K-11A, K-12A, K-15A (1966)

G- 9A MAJOR PACK SET, issued 1962
  1. contains M-1B, M-2B, M-4A, M-6A

G- 9B SERVICE STATION SET, issued 1964
  1. contains 13C, 33B, 71B, A-1B, MG-1B (1964)
  2. contains 13D, 33B, 71B, A-1B, MG-1B (1965)

G-10A GARAGE GIFT SET, issued 1962
1. contains 13C, 25B, 31B, A-1A, MG-1A
2. contains 13C, 25B, 31B, A-1B, MG-1B

G-10B FIRE STATION SET, issued 1964
1. contains 9C, 14C, 59B, MF-1A

POCKET CATALOGS

American and English catalogs are usually the easiest to obtain, with foreign language versions more difficult. Prices are for U.S. or English versions. An addition of 5-20% can be added for some of the foreign editions to these catalogs.

VARIATIONS

1957- depicts No. 1 Road Roller Moko Lesney box
1. 1957- English ($100-150)

1958- depicts No.44A Rolls Royce emerging from its box
1. 1958- U.S.A. ($100-150)

1959- (1st edition) as above but with "1959" edition in upper right
1. U.S.A. (1st edition) ($90-125)

1959- (2nd edition) depicts A-2 Car Transporter, No.43 Hillman Minx & Y-9 Fowler Engine
1. English (2nd edition) ($90-125)

1960- (1st edition) depicts group of regular wheels atop their boxes in a semi-circle inside of catalog depicts #4 tractor, #27 lowloader (most obvious differences)
1. U.S.A., English (1st editions) ($80-95)

1960- (2nd edition) same as above but obvious inside pages depict #4 cycle & #27 Cadillac
1. U.S.A., English (2nd editions) ($80-95)

1961- depicts no. 5 bus
1. U.S.A., English, International, Canada ($60-75)

1962- depicts no. 65 Jaguar 3.4 Litre Sedan
1. U.S.A., English, International, Canada, Germany, French, Italian ($60-75)

1963- depicts no. 53 Mercedes Benz
1. U.S.A., English, French ($40-55)

1964- depicts no. 28 Jaguar Mk. 10
1. U.S.A., Enlgish, International, German, French ($35-50)

1965- depicts racing scene
1. U.S.A., English, International, German, French ($35-50)

1966- depicts several models with London scene
1. U.S.A., English, International, Canada, German, French, Japanese ($20-35)

1967- depicts several regular wheels with different country flags
1. U.S.A., English, International, German, Japanese, French ($15-20)

1968- shows group of models with "1968" in large lettering
1. U.S.A., English, International, German, Japanese, French ($12-18)

1969- shows traffic view from driver perspective
1. U.S.A., English, International, German, Japanese, French, Italian ($8-12)

TRADE OR DEALERS CATALOGS

These were given out at trade fairs or toy fairs and not intended for the collector. Early catalogs are very difficult to find.

1963 ($125-150)

1964 ($125-150)

1965 ($75-90)

1966 ($75-90)

1967 ($40-55)

1968 ($35-50)

1969 ($35-50)

PAINTING BOOKS

Lesney's Painting Books are today very rare. These were a series of coloring books that showed several scenes in color with the matching picture on the opposite page in lined form to be either colored or painted to match. Price Guide Value on any edition: ($75-100)

THE BOX AND THE BLISTERPACK

It was in 1953 that the "Matchbox" name was born. Matchbox is taken from the type of packaging used to package these small little toys--a match box. The original design of the outer matchbox was taken from an old Czechoslovakian matchbox design by Norvic matches. This is shown on the top row and first box shown on the color plate of box types. Early boxes carried the "Moko" legend through 1960. In 1960, Lesney bought out Moko and dissolved the name. The first seven regular wheels exist in script "Moko" boxes and these are very rare today. As time went on the Matchbox box changed to a larger size to accommodate larger models and changed in de-sign. The later boxes eventually included color depictions of the models. In 1964, Lesney Products tried packaging their miniature and its box within a blisterpack. A blisterpack is a package with a card backing in which the contents on the package are contained within a sealed bubble, or blister. This was tried again in 1966. It wasn't until early 1969 that blisterpack Matchbox models were seen in quantity, and within a few years the box that became so important to the "Matchbox" trademark ceased to be packaged within the blistercard. But this will be discussed in a further book.

THE HOME DISPLAY

In 1969, Lesney Products introduced a modular interlocking displaying system known as the "Home Display". Each clear acrylic unit displayed five models and has a removable front cover. Price guide value: $5.00--$8.00

In the last few years, a new modified version of this interlocking system was re-developed by a private firm and re-marketed under the name "Magic Box". The idea and look is almost the same as the "Home Display" but the unit now contains removable shelves that can be adjusted to accommodate slightly larger models. These are currently available from Neil's Wheels, Box 354, Old Bethpage, N.Y. 11804.

PREPRODUCTIONS AND PROTOTYPES

Before a Matchbox model is ever issued, a model must be selected for the range. Usually a real life vehicle is sought out and careful measurements and drawings are made. These are then set to a blue-print. In the early days, prototypes were produced either in resin or even from wood. A prototype is an idea model and occasionally only the single prototype model may be made as it was not lucky enough to be chosen for the Matchbox range. A selection of these models are shown in this book. Occasionally prototypes use existing models to make other models. For example: the Refreshment Canteen prototype actually uses the MB25C Petrol Tanker chassis and this is mounted in reverse. Then resin attachments were added, including two separate and removable resin block containers. The decals used were from the MB37A/B Coca Cola Truck and MB47B Ice Cream Truck.

Once a model is chosen for the range, color trials are usually produced. These are called preproduction models. These models may have slight changes, such as the luggage color of the 56B Fiat 1500 shown or a completely different color to that chosen such as the MB25 Cortina in tan. These models are very rare. Some collectors place very high market values on these items, however it is beyond the scope of this book to place prices on models never actually issued for the market.

FAKES AND COPIES

They say that imitation is the sincerest form of flattery, but when it comes to certain things, such as toys, this can be illegal. Lesney Products had an illegal copy of the A-4 Road Signs made in the early 1960s. These signs, although packaged on a card denoting "Matchbox Series" and "Matchbox" at the bottom of the sign are fakes, or counterfeit, Matchbox toys. The real A-4 signs are diecast metal and number eight in the series. The original signs are boxed and contain the "Lesney" name on the bottom. The fakes are plastic and two sets of six carded signs exist.

Occasionally, you may find "Matchbox" items that pre-date the Lesney company. Two such items include a Match Box Construction set by Louis Marx. The item dating into the 1920s or 1930s is packaged in a similar matchbox style box. Another Matchbox item, date unknown, is a Matchbox boxing figure. This small, crude, Japanese-made figure is also packaged in a similar match box container. A further item comes from Hong Kong and consists of a series of cheap plastic cars and trucks. The box, again is a match box style, with "Match Box Series" printed on the box.

Further copies include some very crude replicas of the first issue regular wheels. These models were sold under the name "Shadow Box." A few examples are shown. Other copies from Russia or Poland included copies from the Yesteryear series including the Y-14 Stutz in all plastic and the Y-6 Cadillac in metal but all chrome plated.

Unlike other toy collectibles, a restored Lesney or Matchbox toy is absolutely *worthless*. This includes all repainted or touched-up vehicles. Tampering in the Matchbox hobby is a no-no. Sometimes "enterprising" persons swap labels, body parts and the like to make up "new" variations. These are not worth anything monetarily. A few examples in this book are shown--12A Land Rover with *gray* plastic wheels, 12C Land Rover Safari in silver, 48B Sports Boats in all white or all red, and 51B 8-Wheel Tipper with orange cab and "Pointer" labels. All are very well "faked" and to unsuspecting novices these could be passed on as original. Always be on the look out, especially on rare items. Check for rivet tampering, fingerprints, brush marks, peeling labels, etc.

MATCHBOX COLLECTORS CLUBS

For those who would like more information on models covered in these books or would like information on newer models as well, a collectors club can be an additional source of information for the Matchbox enthusiast. The following clubs can help you through their newsletters which are published on quarterly, bi-monthly or monthly offerings. Please send a self addressed stamped envelope when writing to the clubs for information.

U.K. MATCHBOX
Founded in 1977. Although no longer in existence, if you are able to get copies of this club's magazine you are in for a wealth of information as supplied by its then editor Ray Bush.

MATCHBOX U.S.A.
Founded in 1977. This club offers a monthly publication with the editor being the author of this book- Charles Mack. Write to: Matchbox U.S.A., 62 Saw Mill Road, Durham, Connecticut 06422

MATCHBOX INTERNATIONAL COLLECTORS ASSOCIATION
Founded in 1985. This club offers a bi-monthly publication. Editors are Stewart Orr and Kevin McGimpsey. For information in North America contact: M.I.C.A. North America, 574 Canewood Crescent, Waterloo, Ontario, N2L 5P6 Canada

AMERICAN INTERNATIONAL MATCHBOX
Founded in 1970 by Harold Colpitts, this monthly newsletter is now being edited by Mrs. Jean Conner. Contact the club at 522 Chestnut Street, Lynn, Massachusetts 01904.

PENNSYLVANIA MATCHBOX COLLECTORS CLUB
Founded in 1980, this monthly newsletter and club offers to those basically in the Pennsylvania area, but membership is open to all Matchbox collectors. Write to the club secretary: Bill Charles, 2015 Old Philadelphia Pike, Lancaster, Pennsylvania 17602.

MATCHBOX COLLECTORS CLUB
Originally founded in 1966, this newsletter ceased publication in 1982 but was reformed in 1989 by Charles Mack in a quarterly format. Write to P.O. Box 278, Durham, Connecticut 06422.

BAY AREA MATCHBOX COLLECTORS CLUB
Founded in 1971. Basically geared to those collectors in the California area. Contact: BAMCA, P.O. Box 1534, San Jose, California 95109.

CHESAPEAKE MINIATURE VEHICLE COLLECTORS CLUB
Founded in 1978. A collectors club devoted to all miniature cars including Matchbox. Contact at 7121 Lorry Lane, Lanham, Maryland 20706.

BIBLIOGRAPHY

Bowdidge, Philip. *Matchbox Gift Sets 1957-1988*, Philip Bowdidge, 8 Melrose Court, Ashley New Milton, Hants, BH25 5BY, England, 1988

_____. *Matchbox Major and Accessory Pack Series*, Philip Bowdidge, 8 Melrose Court, Ashley, New Milton, Hants BH25 5BY, England, 1988

Cramer, Rock and Smith, James. *Matchbox Catalogs*, 3104 Mesa Drive, El Paso, Texas 79901 and 431 George Cross Dr., Norman, Oklahoma 73069, 1989

Mack, Charles. *Matchbox Models of Yesteryear*, Matchbox USA publication, 62 Saw Mill Road, Durham, Connecticut 06422, 1989

Schiffer, Nancy. *Matchbox Toys*, Schiffer Publishing Ltd., P.O. Box E, Exton, Pennsylvania 19341, 1982

Stannard, Michael. *Matchbox 1-75 Series 1953-1969*, Three M's Productions, 37K New Road, Spalding, Lincs., PE11 1DW, England, 1985